Trust
Betrayed

Trust Betrayed

THE TRUTH BEHIND THE ORGAN RETENTION SCANDAL IN IRELAND

KARINA COLGAN

POOLBEG

Published 2009
by Poolbeg Books Ltd
123 Grange Hill, Baldoyle
Dublin 13, Ireland
E-mail: poolbeg@poolbeg.com

1 3 5 7 9 10 8 6 4 2

A catalogue record for this book is available from the British Library.

ISBN 978-1-84223-374-0

Typeset by Patricia Hope in Sabon 11.5/15.5
Printed by CPI Mackays, Chatham ME5 8TD, UK

www.poolbeg.com

The identities of some people written about in this book have been disguised in accordance with professional standards of confidentiality to afford their right to privileged communication with the author and retain their anonymity.

About the Author

Karina Colgan lives in south Dublin. She has worked as a journalist for the past sixteen years and as a magazine publisher for six. She is the bestselling and acclaimed author of three other books: *Hear My Silence: Overcoming Depression*; *You Have to Scream with Your Mouth Shut: Violence in the Home* and *If It Happens To You: Miscarriage and Stillbirth – A Human Insight*. She is currently working on her next book, which will be published later this year. Karina has always been an ardent campaigner for social injustice, indeed injustice of any kind, and from a young age has been involved in many organisations, fighting both national and global injustice. You can e-mail Karina at: trustbetrayed@eircom.net or hearmysilence@eircom.net. Karina's recent book *Hear My Silence* was received to acclaimed reviews and is said to really help people come to terms with depression. It is available through bookshops nationwide and also by mail order through Poolbeg Press at www.poolbeg.com.

Do not stand at my grave and weep;
I am not there. I do not sleep.
I am a thousand winds that blow.
I am the diamond glints on snow.
I am the sunlight on ripened grain.
I am the gentle autumn rain.
When you awaken in the morning's hush,
I am the swift uplifting rush
Of quiet birds in circled flight.
I am the soft stars that shine at night.
Do not stand at my grave and cry;
I am not there. I did not die.

(Although generally attributed to Mary Frye, this poem is accredited to various authors.)

"God's finger touched him, and he slept."

ALFRED LORD TENNYSON

This book is dedicated to my darling son Glen Colgan. With my first book I gave you immortality; with this one I give you, and all those affected by this awful scandal, back the dignity that was so cruelly snatched from you in death. I also hope I have given you, and all those whose voices will never be heard, justice and answers. It's the very least you deserve and the last thing I can do for you. I've kept my promise; so perhaps now, my precious son, you can finally rest in peace.

CONTENTS

FOREWORD

Charlotte Yeates, Founder, Parents for Justice

In December 1999, families in Ireland learned to their horror that the organs of their children and loved ones had been removed during post mortem, then retained and disposed of without the knowledge or consent of the parents or next of kin. Later these families found out that in some cases the pituitary glands of their loved ones had been *sold* to pharmaceutical companies to make a growth hormone medication for children with stunted growth.

It is now a decade since this national scandal came to light and although there has been media coverage about this issue, there are still a large number of people in the state who are not familiar with it. Indeed, some people think that this practice was either confined to Dublin or to children.

The truth is that this was the practice all over the country and it involved adults as well as children (including stillborn children). Despite the fact that this Government established an inquiry into Post Mortem Practices and Procedures in the State in 2000, and despite the fact that in excess of €20 million has been spent on this private inquiry, the families affected by the scandal have learned nothing at all. They are still waiting to find out what happened to the organs of their children and loved ones after they were removed.

One of the people who did learn about the organ retention scandal was Karina Colgan, the author of this book. Karina's story is similar to many thousands of families in this country – except that during the writing of this book she unexpectedly had to bury her son for the second time, after inadvertently finding out that sixty-two parts of him were still in the hospital and his brain elsewhere. With every ounce of strength she had left, she made the decision to continue to write this book to let people know the true story of how this horrific practice has impacted on many Irish families and how these families are still suffering. This book will also make it perfectly clear that there are many more families in Ireland who do not yet realise that they are also involved. *It is believed that any person who has had a post mortem in any hospital or institution in Ireland is potentially involved. To this very day (2009), there are unclaimed organs in Irish hospitals and institutions.*

However, the only way families will find out is to make their own enquiries to the individual hospital or institution. The hospitals or institutions will not offer the information voluntarily. If, on reading this book, a person decides to make these enquiries, Karina will have been responsible for allowing families to make that choice and access the information they wish to. Karina has included a chapter on how to find out if a loved one has been affected (see Chapter 15).

This choice was taken away from families all over Ireland when the medical profession, with their paternalistic attitude of "doctor knows best", decided to keep parents and families in the dark and not tell them what would happen to their child or loved one during post mortem. In doing this, they also denied the families any comfort they may have received if they had been allowed to freely donate organs for research or teaching purposes. They also used tactics against those who had been affected in an effort to keep them quiet and not let it leak to the media, which you may read about further on.

"Consent" is a small word but has a huge meaning. Many parents and families have said that if their consent had been sought for organ retention in an open and honest way, that is "informed consent", they would have allowed their loved ones' organs to be retained for teaching or research purposes, if it would have helped another person in the future.

They would not, however, have allowed their loved ones' organs to be retained if they were to be sold to pharmaceutical companies, or if they were to be left in buckets on hospital shelves for years rendering them useless. Unfortunately, this is what happened in a very large number of cases. It is little wonder, then, that families are still angry and upset. This Government promised us answers but all they gave us was lies and silence; we are still waiting for these elusive answers we were promised ten years ago.

It would be remiss of me not to thank Karina for having the courage and tenacity to write this long overdue book, which in many ways would not have been possible without her. Karina had to go through the trauma of a second funeral midway through writing this book – the shock must have been unimaginable and I cannot understand what it must have been like for her to come back from her son's funeral and to have to start to rewrite a book that was almost finished.

It is hard to believe it is a book that is factual and not some form of fiction. It is a book without an ending . . . yet. It is a book that shows the plight of human suffering. It is a book that shows the drive and determination of the parents and families to continue to fight for justice and answers, no matter how long this takes. It is a book that remembers beautiful children and family members and makes the reader see that they were not just "sets of human organs", but loving and laughing human beings who brought joy to our families and will always be remembered with love and tenderness.

I know that God will take care of them all for us.

Charlotte Yeates
Founder, Parents for Justice

ACKNOWLEDGEMENTS

I would like to begin by saying that I am not a medical, political, legal or academic expert and this is not a medical, political, legal or academic book. It is a book about people like you and me, for the most part, unknowingly caught up in a scandal that has been kept hidden from the public as much as possible since it first broke in 1999. I am aware of a case in 1998, but the family decided not to come forward, as is their right.

In ways, this book is almost a sequel to my first book, *If It Happens to You: Miscarriage and Stillbirth – A Human Insight* (A & A Farmar), which was written at a time when I was completely oblivious to the barbarity of the post mortem practice. This book is prompted by and is dedicated to my son, Glen. I hope somehow he knows how very many lives he touched and the huge contribution he has made to change in his brief life. However, it would not be the book it is without the support of many people, and it is with gratitude that I take this opportunity to thank them and all those who were affected.

It would be impossible to write two books simultaneously on intensely personal, emotive and indeed controversial issues without the love and support of my exceptionally special family, whom I am blessed to have and who make all I do possible. They are the wind beneath my wings. It is for this reason that I acknowledge them first. To my children Karl and Sarah: you are loved more than you will ever know and I am so very proud of both of you and of all you have achieved. You have grown into adults I am proud to call my son and daughter. To my mother Tina, my mentor, who brought me up to believe that anything is possible if you put your mind to it. She was a great help with copy typing and without her I would not be here! To my sister Tammy, who is always there when I need her, whether to offer advice, to give support and straight-talking and for being a sister I am fortunate to have. To my nephews Sam (my Godson) (10); Mark (8), Owen (8) and Paul (6), who all saved up to give me a very big, bright yellow lollipop, which has a smiley face and the words "Have a Nice Day", to put on my desk and make me smile when I started this book. Thanks, boys, it worked, just like Jelly Ted did for my last book. In fact they are best friends now and will go nowhere without each other! Lastly, I again reserve my biggest thanks for my husband, Gerry, who is unquestionably my better half and a person at times I wish I could be more like. Thank you for being the very special person that you are and for putting up with me; I am not the easiest person to live with.

To Tanya-Samantha and Anna Coogan; to my friend Lorraine, her daughter Amanda, and son "Baby John" (RIP), who will never be forgotten. What we have shared over the past twenty-one years makes her a special friend. To my

Guardian Angel in New York, Camille Colon, Joe and her adorable dog Juido – you know why I am thanking you. This thank you is from the bottom of my heart – you have shown me the meaning of unconditional and true friendship.

I would also like to thank all those who took the trouble to send flowers, get well cards, Mass Bouquets and chocolates to the hospital and to the house, after my recent and unexpected illness – all were very much appreciated.

To all my other friends, and in particular Michelle and Bernie, for dropping in constantly to see how I was and for not giving up even though you rarely got past the front door! Anna actually did this one evening, so I had little choice but let her in. Thanks also to Garda Chaplain Fr Joe Kennedy, who officiated at Glen's funeral with very little notice and offered to come to the hospital and bless me. I would like to thank Ellish O'Donnell, Head Social Worker, for attending Glen's blessing, though ironically the Master was unable to attend due to a meeting with HSE CEO Professor Brendan Drumm. I would also like to take this opportunity to thank Anna Farmar who saw that spark and took a chance by publishing my first book – something I will always be grateful to her for. In a way it was a first for both of us: I read her book, *Children's Last Days*, per chance and decided to write the one I had needed but which didn't exist. I wrote to Anna with a very brief outline; she read the first few pages I sent her and said yes. I had never written a book and she had never published one, so we made a good team! The rest, as they say, is history!

I would also like to extend my profuse thanks to Parents for Justice (PFJ), particularly in a private capacity to Charlotte Yeates and Ann Docherty, who have become good friends. This book would not be the book it is without them. I am particularly grateful for their friendship, time, expertise and assistance, as well as for the countless cups of coffee, biscuits and Ann's delicious homemade cakes. (Ann even baked me a most delicious coffee cake, for Mother's Day, which became known in the house as *mine*! She also baked me cakes to build my strength up after I was ill.)

Their hospitality and availability around the clock were second to none and anything they could do to help they did. There were many nights we sat around tables and floors strewn with papers, files and Freedom of Information documents in a quest to find answers. Any answers. Late night telephone calls were common, too. It is hard to believe that almost a decade has passed since I first met Charlotte sitting in the Plaza Hotel in 2000, and it seems harder still to believe I have not known Ann for this length of time, given the close friendship we have developed. They were the first people I went to when I found out about Glen for the second time recently and they were a tower of strength to me. I knew that they knew exactly what I was talking about and how I felt and I had no fear of what I was saying sounding stupid.

My most sincere thanks also go to all those who shared their stories and also to PFJ members, who were there when I needed them and answered any questions I had. PFJ is an organisation nobody wants membership of, but those who are members battle the odds undeterred.

My thanks also go to Michel Aarden in Holland who kept regular tabs on me and flew over with his wife Cora for the launch of my last book (Happy 40th, Michel, for 10 May; I didn't forget!); to Riccardo Carlo in Italy for his constant texts and calls to see how I am and for his invitation to Rome with Anna; to Sharon Fagan, who has done me favours at the drop of a hat; to Ruth Killeen, who does Trojan work on a professional and personal basis on my behalf – I cannot adequately articulate all she has done for me. I would also like to thank the generosity of Phyllis Murphy, who was a complete stranger who went out of her way to help.

I would also like to extend my personal gratitude to those who shared their heart-breaking stories with me – painful as it was for them to do so and painful as it was for me to listen to them. I laughed with them as we recalled funny moments; I cried with them when we remembered sad ones and every night I lay in bed and remembered; for every journey they made back was a journey back for me.

I would like to extend my professional and personal thanks to His Holiness, Pope Benedict XVI and the Vatican for their valuable insight and for responding to my letter so promptly (it is the only non-religious book we are aware of to which His Holiness has made a contribution, a fact we are very proud of); to Dr Denis Cusack – in my eyes a visionary, and President of the Coroners' Society of Ireland – with whom I had a very long chat one evening. He got fed up waiting for the wheels of bureaucracy so he started his own website, as did Dublin Coroner Dr Brian Farrell, as he proudly told me – the first in the country and well worth a visit. Their website addresses are listed at the back of this book and make invaluable reading for those wishing to find out more about the role of a coroner and the post mortem process. I have also included a short section on medical jargon in Chapter 10 with the kind assistance of Michelle Maher of St James's Hospital. I would like to extend my professional thanks to the many other experts, far too numerous to mention – you know who you are and how very grateful I am.

I would like to thank those who gave so freely of their time and expertise – including those in the medical and legal professions and, in particular, Professor Michael Geary, outgoing Master, Rotunda Hospital; Dr Martin Daly, President, Irish Medical Association (IMO); Eilish McDonnell, Chief Social Worker, Rotunda Hospital; Michelle Mayer of St James's Hospital; Royal College of Surgeons in Ireland (RCSI); Liam Doran, General Secretary, Irish Nurses Organisation (INO); Dr Donald McCarthy, Consultant Haematologist, Director of Pathology, St Vincent's University Hospital, Consultant Haematologist St Luke's Hospital Dublin and a great email buddy; Dr Peter Boylan, former Master of Holles Street (although still there, he is now involved with a number of different facets of obstetrics such as home birth and participating in Q & A sessions online. Coincidentally, Peter wrote the foreword to my first book!); Mark Murphy, CEO, Irish Kidney Association (IKA); Dr Deirdre Madden, author of the Madden Report; Dr Robert Towers; Dr Denis Cusack, President of the Coroners' Society of Ireland; Dr Brian Farrell, Dublin

City Coroner and a great help; Dr Chris Fitzpatrick, Master of the Coombe; Dr John Gillian, pathologist, Rotunda, for our very recent one-to-one conversation during which he answered every quetion on my list in an unrushed way, even drawing diagrams and showing me various pathological instruments; Dr Lorcan Birthistle, CEO, Our Lady's Hospital, Crumlin; Dr James Lee who has seen me through thick and thin; Dr Maura Milner from all those years ago. I said I would never foget you and all you did and I haven't; Senator Feargal Quinn; Dr Maura Milner, Rob Bracken; the Garda Press Office and individuals within and indeed outside it. You know who you are. I would like also to acknowledge the co-operation of RTÉ Archives and the *Irish Independent*. I would like to acknowledge the calm demeanour of Richard Malone from eircom, who managed to get my email working again after many hours, when I was at my wits' end. Thanks Richard, you were a life-saver on the night.

I would like to take this opportunity to pay tribute to two PFJ founder members who have sadly passed away – Fionnuala O'Reilly and Margaret McKeever. May they both rest in peace with their beloved children, knowing we shall continue their fight for truth and justice, however long it takes. Tragically, the baby girl, Mary-Kate, born to Breda and Joe Butler lost her battle for life on 29th October 2008; may she rest in peace.

I extend thanks to long-time friends E O'D, Colm Dempsey and Dermot O'Donnell, who are always at the other end of a phone to answer my questions and give advice or at least put me in touch with someone who can. My thanks also to certain TDs whose comments were most helpful; you also know who you are and I ask that you take this as a token of my appreciation. Writing this book has confirmed many things, but perhaps the most important thing it has confirmed is that I am certainly not alone in wanting justice.

I would like to take this opportunity to thank the doctors and staff who treated me after my sudden illness, particularly all those on the Lynn Ward.

Finally, to all the team at Poolbeg, and in particular to my editor Brian Langan, who did what they do best and turned this into a book I am proud of.

INTRODUCTION

"Truth is not only violated by falsehood; it may be equally outraged by silence."

HENRI FREDERIC AMELIA

I thought long and hard about how to write the introduction for this book, but deep down I knew that there was only one option, which was to write it honestly and from the heart. I am not writing this as a hardened journalist, for I cannot write about this horrific scandal in a detached or dispassionate way; nor would I want to. This is a subject that is intensely personal to me. I also believe people have a right to know what went on and what continues to go on to this day. In this book I am a mother foremost and a writer second.

In the most agonising twist of fate and the cruellest irony imaginable, midway through writing this book I accidentally discovered that *sixty-two sections/tissues of my son were still in the hospital and his brain was missing.* The Master could not tell me any more because he was unable to locate any record of this: "*I can confirm that there is no record of what organs/tissues of Glen's were incinerated or when . . .*" The date on the page was *7th November 2008.* You may read the rest of this letter in Chapter 1.

This starkly brought home the fact that we are not talking about something that happened decades ago. Upon reading his words, I was transported back in time so quickly; it literally took my breath away and I could feel my heart begin to palpitate. Firstly, I was taken back to 2001, when I had returned to the hospital to be told that Glen's organs had been incinerated a number of years previously, without my knowledge or consent; at this time I did not realise that his brain and other tissues and parts still remained there without my knowledge or consent, nor was I informed.

I had started writing this book without this knowledge, so the shock was severe. Amid the grief of having to hold a second funeral, I knew that, no matter what it took, I would finish this book. This was my third visit to the hospital since my son was born and his second funeral.

I spoke to Mr Michael Geary, Master of the hospital, at length, because I now knew that everything I had been told to this point was entirely questionable. Unfortunately, he was unable to answer most of my questions because, incredibly, *the hospital kept no records* (a common occurrence in most of the twenty-six hospitals involved). I would like to point out that Mr Geary was not the Master at the time Glen's organs were removed and he gave me every assistance in answering every question I asked and apologised again because he could not do more.

How can one get answers to questions when no records exist? However, a far more pertinent question must be asked: *why do no such records exist?* Unfortunately, I had built quite a good rapport with Mr Geary, only to discover that his tenure was coming to an end and that he was being replaced by a new Master, Sam Coulter Smith, in January 2009. I arranged a meeting with Mr Coulter Smith, whom I have yet had the opportunity to meet.

I believe the majority of people in Ireland have no idea what the organ retention scandal is, because it has been censored to pieces and kept as quiet as possible and, above all else, kept impersonal and detached. In the main, faces were not put to statistics, making it easier to desensitise people and play the issue down.

My objective with this book is to remove the censoring, to share the personality of just a minute fraction of the victims, and, above all else, to get answers and ensure that Human Tissue legislation is enacted without any further delay. One has to say, God forgive all those who have been in a position to ratify such legislation over the last decade.

Unauthorised organ retention is an uncomfortable subject even to think about. This book highlights the true horror of the barbaric and ethically questionable practice, which took place in many hospitals across the country, of removing and retaining organs from babies, children and adults without consent – for research, for sale and, often, for no reason at all. As a mother who has been affected by this scandal a number of times, my focus is drawn to babies and children.

However, I ask that you pause to bear in mind that *thousands of organs were also taken from adults.* I briefly allude later to the case of Tommy, a much-loved husband and father, whose wife Ann fought on long after others would have stopped; and Ciara, a much-loved daughter, sibling and friend, who was just embarking on her studies. I have included both – among others – as they were not recognised because they failed to fall into the ludicrously restrictive age bracket of the Madden Report, which was that they had to be born alive and died at twelve years old or under.

After consulting with the parents and relatives, I made the decision to include the pictures of the tiny proportion of the victims whose stories are told in this book so that this awful scandal is made "real" to the reader. Each of the children and adults you see in this book was *violated and decimated in death, stripped of their dignity and buried incomplete* – without the knowledge of their loved ones.

Pause and close your eyes – for just a moment. Can you imagine your child or loved one in this book? How would you feel? How would you feel knowing that perhaps the toddler who once giggled and sucked his thumb at night had had sand or cotton wool soaked in solution placed in his body to disguise the weight of his missing organs? Or the baby you breastfed to give her the best possible start in life had her pituitary glands removed and sold to pharmaceutical companies? (These, along with the glands of many other babies would then have been stored in a freezer supplied by the pharmaceutical company, ready for collection and payment by sales reps from those companies.)

Could you bear to bury your precious child twice, like I had to? My son's brain has yet to be found (along with other organs). It is for this reason that I resolutely refuse to put his name on his headstone until I am satisfied I have done all I can do to put as much of him back together as is humanly possible.

The parents and loved ones of the people in this book told their stories, and I have written about them, in the hope that people will realise that this happened to ordinary people in late twentieth-century Ireland. The ramifications of this scandal have carried into twenty-first-century Ireland (2009 and no doubt beyond) and those who, for a whole decade, have sought only the truth, still battle. By the time this book hits the shelves, it will be a full decade since this scandal broke and we are still no nearer to the answers we sought in 1999. Parents were the last to know – and then it was only by chance – that their children had been taken apart and never put back together.

Two particular pharmaceutical companies involved, which are named in the Madden Report and also later in this book, confirmed that they purchased thousands of pituitary glands from hospitals around the country over a period of decades (Madden cites over 14,000 pituitary glands in her Report, which is only the tip of the iceberg). The practice stopped only in 1985 when a synthetic replacement was made and there was no longer a need for human pituitary glands. However, it later transpired that a batch of human growth hormone was contaminated with variant Creutzfeldt-Jakob Disease (vCJD), a rare and incurable degenerative neurological disorder that is ultimately fatal; it affects about one person in one million. There is evidence to suggest that the practice of using human pituitary glands may one day recommence under the right circumstances.

I have read through countless reports and documents; I have seen invoices and orders for glands; and I have seen the cheques that were paid for them. Not surprisingly, the names of the individuals to whom the cheques were made payable, which were obtained under the Freedom of Information Act, were obliterated and indecipherable. Freedom of Information? I couldn't find any information.

Indeed, the tragic case of baby Orlaith Conway was cited as an example of this in Private Members' Business in the Dáil just a few short years ago, on 22nd October 2002. Although in the public domain, I would like to thank Róisín McCormack for her blessing to use this piece, which clearly illustrates what politicians have been aware of for years. I wrote to them also.

Róisín Conway's beautiful daughter was born on 23rd June 1998. She was a happy and contented baby who brought her family much joy. However, little Orlaith was tragically a victim of sudden infant death on 16th September 1998. As she had died suddenly at home, she was taken to a leading Dublin hospital, where the decision was taken to perform a coroner's post mortem. Her parents never received any details of the autopsy.

However, when details of the organ retention scandal first came to light, like so many other people, Róisín contacted the hospital to enquire whether any of Orlaith's organs had been taken. Her worst fears were realised when she was told that a number of Orlaith's organs had been retained by the hospital. When Róisín and her husband returned to the hospital to get the missing organs, *they were given two white plastic buckets containing the organs of their precious baby daughter.*

In the Dáil, John Gormley TD responded by saying:

The death of a child evokes emotions so raw and so searing that it is almost unbearable. I know from talking to bereaved parents that such a death is accompanied by guilt so enormous that it engulfs every moment of every day. There are the memories of holding that tiny fragile being for the final farewell. These are painful, sacrosanct memories. They are part of the fabric of a cherished child's life and death.

Now fast forward five years, ten years, fifteen years or twenty years. Let us imagine we discover that our most cherished child's body has been plundered, violated in the most grotesque manner imaginable. This has been the experience of the parents in the Public Gallery this evening. Each family has its own harrowing tale to tell, a tale of a life cut short, a future denied and a tiny fragile defenceless body desecrated and violated on a cold slab in a hospital laboratory.

There is the case of a mother and father who sat in a hospital consulting room five years after their son's death and who learned the boy's organs were at that moment sitting on a hospital shelf, down the corridor. How can we even begin to understand how horrific it must be to sit in a consultant's room and be told that parts of your most cherished baby are being preserved in a bucket of formaldehyde in a room nearby? Can anybody even begin to understand the impact that the unauthorised removal, retention and disposal of human organs by Irish hospitals has had on thousands of families throughout the State?

Can anybody begin to understand the trauma of discovering that one's most precious child has been relegated to the status of a spare part in a hospital laboratory? Can we even try to comprehend the agony of a family that then has to retrieve these organs and endure a second funeral.

It is truly astonishing that we are no nearer to elucidating answers or knowing the truth than we were when this speech was made by John Gormley in 2002 (and when I in such a second funeral buried some more of her baby in November 2008).

What is equally shocking is that, when this scandal broke, neither hospitals nor health boards made contact with parents. In fact, they were advised not to and at an Eastern Regional Health Authority meeting in 2004 – while the Anne Dunne Inquiry was ongoing – it was decided, after a brief three-week public "awareness" campaign, that unclaimed organs would be buried. The terms of reference of the Dunne Inguiry included the removal, retention *and disposal* of human organs. These organs should not have been touched, no matter what was said by the HSE or the Department of Health.

They did agree that they would dig the organs back up if parents came looking for them. If parents wanted to find out if their loved one had been violated, they had to go looking for information, which initially was often not forthcoming from the various hospitals involved. In fact, some hospitals went to court in a bid to prevent having to hand over information. Parents for Justice were told about this "public awareness campaign" – on 19th December 2007. They requested copies of newspaper advertisements and posters and the like, but never received these.

In an article in the *New York Times* on 21st March 2004, Master of the National Maternity Hospital in Holles Street, Dr Declan Keane, was quoted as saying: "The extent of the organ retention was a shock even to people in the profession." This same hospital retained thousands of children's body parts for research purposes and also sold pituitary glands to pharmaceutical companies. Additionally, Holles Street also went to the Supreme Court in an effort to evade having to give information or hand over records to the Dunne Inquiry. (I should qualify this by saying that the practice of supplying pituitary glands to pharmaceutical companies had ceased long before Dr Keane became Master of Holles Street.)

Like many others affected by this scandal, I am angry, shocked, appalled, and repulsed at the atrocious manner in which parents and families have been treated and by the fact that they have consistently been denied information they have a right to.

As a firm advocate of medical research, I questioned whether, perhaps, ignorance and a misplaced concept of research was somehow responsible. However, I reasonably concluded that doctors and pathologists have a level of intelligence that enables them to distinguish between what is right and what is wrong. As what went on was clearly wrong, I deduced that this was not the reason.

Medical ethics are based on the Hippocratic Oath – which is now often referred to as the "Hypocritical Oath", because modern medicine has deviated so far from the tenets of the original oath that it bears little resemblance to it. The Geneva Medical Book, drawn up in 1948 by the World Health Organisation, adopted a more modern form of the Hippocratic Oath, which simply states: "I shall keep absolute respect for human life from the moment of conception." Doctors who took this oath (and others like it) went on to violate and decimate babies, children and adults in death.

I looked hard for conscience and moral paradigm, but found none. Try as I did, I could not resolve that, in good moral and medical conscience, doctors and pathologists could do this. I do not yet know the reason why it happened and it is inconceivable that, until a few years ago, the practice was still going on in hospitals across Ireland.

For a decade, those affected have been seeking answers that, to this day, have not been forthcoming, despite many millions of euro being spent on inquiries that have failed to produce anything substantive and have been clouded in secrecy. The initial Dunne Inquiry (a non-statutory inquiry) chaired by Anne Dunne SC, was conducted in private, took four years and was wound up, unfinished, without ever producing a report or any findings . . . at an estimated cost of €20 million (of taxpayers' money, let me add). *This is the first and only time in the history of the State that an inquiry has been closed down without producing a publishable report – a fact worthy of note.*

Some fifty-four boxes of documentation were then stored in a warehouse at a cost to the Office of Public Works (i.e. the taxpayer) of €800 per month, where they remain today, gathering dust. Minister for Health Mary Harney was accused in the media at the time of hiding behind the then Attorney-General, Ruairi Brady, who decided that, in the interests of natural justice, these 3,500 pages of documents could not be publicly released. This poses the pertinent question: natural justice for whom, exactly? Certainly not the parents, nor the loved ones who were left behind to *literally pick up the pieces*.

This debacle was further compounded – at yet more expense: €400,000 to be precise – when Dr Deirdre Madden, a medical ethics expert, was appointed by the Department of Health and Children to produce a report based on the findings of the defunct Dunne Inquiry. The ensuing Madden Report was presented to Minister Harney in December 2005 and released to the public early in 2006. It presented the facts relating to post mortem practice in Ireland (including organ retention). You can download the Madden Report free of charge from: www.dohc.ie/publications/madden.html.

However – and you may draw your own conclusions – this highly restrictive report concentrated on only *three* Dublin hospitals instead of the twenty-six named in the report *and took the decision to recognise only children born alive and under twelve years between 1970 and 2000.* The Geneva Convention clearly sets out the age of adulthood as eighteen. The Madden Report *did not* take into account stillborn babies or children between the ages of twelve and eighteen, or indeed adults, which would have *dramatically* increased the figures upon which the report was based. In my opinion, this is misleading and grossly underestimates the true scale of this horrific scandal.

I wondered to myself who on earth decided that children become adults at the age of thirteen? After reading through the Madden Report quite a number of times, it was difficult to find any answers to the questions that I and other affected people have – such as, where are our children's organs? Indeed, three years on, many of the report's fifty recommendations have *not yet been implemented.* I include them at the end of Chapter 6.

Parents for Justice were "very confused" by the Madden Report because many of its recommendations do not contain much of what was contained in the findings of Dunne. It was widely reported that Dunne did *not* make any findings. The Madden Report also failed to answer what exactly happened to the organs or where indeed they were or are. The Madden Report for the most part dealt with the future while ignoring the past. However, I did contact Dr Deirdre Madden for the purpose of this book and she did speak with me briefly. (You may read her answers in Chapter 10.)

It is worth noting that PFJ had to obtain the Executive Summary of Evidence, written by Anne Dunne, under the Freedom of Information Act (as distinct from the findings, which came later) and, even then, all names of hospitals and individuals had been destroyed. I obtained a copy of these reports and, as you will read further on, quite frankly it was a waste of my time. Having to elicit information in this way was described at the time by Labour's health spokesperson, Liz McManus, as "ludicrous". She called for the report to be published immediately.

On 18th January 2006, the then Tánaiste and present Minister for Health and Children, Mary Harney, described the Madden Report as "robust" and said that legislation to deal with the issue would be "drafted speedily . . ."

Ten years on, we await the legislation Micheál Martin promised when the scandal first broke. *Over three years on* we await Harney's "speedy legislation" promised after the Madden Report. This delay in information and truth is, I believe, to protect those responsible; not an act of kindness born out of any need to try to "protect" parents. I am far from alone in my belief, as you will read from the many TDs and others who responded to and supported me.

Our imaginations, coupled with known facts, have conjured up nightmare scenarios, which are likely to be far worse than any truth could be. Indeed, my own story bears witness to this.

In this book I present my findings – the facts, and the true stories of just a minute proportion of those who have been affected by this horrific scandal, including my own. No more, no less. In fact, in many cases I have toned them down rather than sensationalise them and upset readers any further than necessary. I have no desire to be judge and jury; I am confident readers will have the ability to come to their own conclusions. I would never have known about the hospital retaining more of Glen and his brain missing, which meant having to undergo a second funeral in November 2008, unless I had accidentally stumbled upon the information. Even after all that has gone on over the past decade, I questioned if anything has been learned in all this time? I spoke with all the Masters of the Dublin maternity hospitals to see what, if anything, had changed. I am pleased to report that a lot *has* changed and the hospitals and hospital personnel have learned lessons, which you may read about further on in this book.

In an effort to establish the truth and ensure that this can never happen again, through the introduction of a human tissue act, I asked the vast majority of TDs in the Dáil the same five questions, which I list at the start of Chapter 12. I had an extremely high response rate. Not surprisingly, most TDs agreed with me, some stuck rigidly to a response prepared especially by the Department of Health for me for TDs to replicate in their replies to me, which I also reproduce in Chapter 12. Some TDs said they would also like to hear the answers to my questions from those in a position to give them. Other TDs were livid at the way things have been covered up and others had their own theories.

Chapter 12, "Politically Speaking", is an interesting chapter because it shows exactly how politicians, including those involved at the time the scandal broke, view this scandal. It also highlights the matter's importance, or rather lack of importance, to those in power both at the time and now, a decade and three successive Health Ministers later.

Truth; it is such a simple word and such an important word. However, until it is told, we will never have closure. From the blacked-out pages I went through, it is impossible to attribute anything to any individual, to a point – which is exactly the purpose of blacking them out. Why were they blacked out? What did they not want revealed?

I would now like to take this opportunity again to add my own request for a statutory public inquiry to all the other requests, including requests from TDs and Parents for Justice, which have to date been denied or ignored.

One has to question what is being hidden not only from the parents, but also from politicians and the Irish people. In fact, I believe it could be even further reaching than this. If nothing is being covered up, what is the difficulty in telling the truth? What is the problem with publishing reports paid for from taxpayers' money? What is the problem with making information public? We are, after all, citizens of what is supposed to be a democratic country.

Sadly, there are families out there who still are not aware of what may have happened to their loved ones and who may realise it only after reading this book. Should you wish to find out if your loved one was affected, Chapter 15 will guide you through what you can do to find out.

Unfortunately, this book may not answer all your questions, nor give closure, but it should inform you what the organ retention scandal was and continues to be. Someone is culpable and *someone must be held accountable*.

It must be remembered that we are talking about many tens of thousands of people who have gone before us, thousands who are there now – and, sadly, the many thousands who will find out after reading this book. There is also the fact of the €20 *million* of taxpayers' money spent, while sick people lie on trolleys in hospital corridors because of bed shortages in hospitals across the country.

As someone who has been there and had to bury the same child twice because of it, I hope this book will contribute to the establishment of human tissue legislation and a public inquiry, which is a decade overdue. This was promised both verbally and in writing by the then Minister for Health, Micheál Martin. Mary Harney, the present Minister for Health and Children, has given repeated assurances about "speedy legislation", yet chose *not* to comment in this book, which as Minister for Health and Children and as a person at the absolute epicentre of this scandal, I find incredibly strange. One would have assumed she would have welcomed the opportunity of being able to address such a large and targeted audience.

This is 2009 and body parts are still being returned to parents a decade after the scandal first broke in this country. Lives and families are sill being torn apart and funerals continue to take place long after a person has died. No parent or loved one should have to go through this agony again and again when there are people out there who can give answers. They should be allowed closure and to lay their loved ones to rest. To date, unlike in the UK, *nobody has been held accountable*. Most of the recommendations of the 2006 Madden Report have yet to be implemented. This is barbaric; all we have had are delays, silence and inaction.

The time for answers is *now*; the time for silence is *over*. We want – *actually, we demand* – answers. Our determination for truth and justice has not diminished with time, *but our impatience is growing*. Perhaps if we make this a political issue where votes enter the equation, we will see progress; although sad, it is probably true. *Let me make it clear, politics is an avenue I am prepared to go down and with the prospect of a General Election looming, it is an opportune time for me to change career.*

I am not going to go away, PFJ is not going to go away, nor are we going to give up or be intimidated. We want answers, we want truth, we want the Dunne Inquiry made public and we want human tissue legislation enacted. Furthermore, we want all of this without further delay. We are *not* going to stop until we get the information we want.

Karina Colgan
April 2009

PREFACE

"It's the same each time with progress. First they ignore you, then they say you're mad, then dangerous, then there's a pause and then you can't find anyone who disagrees with you."

TONY BENN

This has not been an easy book to write; nor will it be an easy book to read. The incomprehensible and horrific matter of unauthorised organ retention is something that has not entered the public domain in any easily understood way *per se* . . . until now. I make no excuse for the shocking and sometimes extremely graphic details you will read.

Throughout this book I am going to take you on a journey that you couldn't imagine in your worst nightmares and then, I'm going to remind you, time and time again, you are *not* reading a work of fiction. What you are reading is *real*. What happened in the unauthorised organ retention scandal happened to ordinary people, who were then treated and continue to be treated in an extraordinary way.

The support I have received writing this book has been nothing short of phenomenal – from family and friends, from Parents for Justice, from the medical profession, from the legal profession, from clerics, from politicians, from complete strangers, from my publishers – the list goes on . . . Like me, there are many thousands of people who want to know what lies in those fifty-four boxes in Blanchardstown and, perhaps more importantly, why have they not been made public? *Did Anne Dunne do too good a job? Is something being covered up that is likely to cause consternation and possibly uprising in the Government? Am I about to open a Pandora's Box?*

I sure hope so; perhaps it will induce answers. It has proved a darn expensive box to open both in terms of money and in terms of human suffering for the thousands affected by it. Just before finishing this book – as if a second funeral wasn't enough to contend with – I was rushed to hospital in March with possible signs of a stroke – a lumbar puncture could not rule out a TIA and an MRI scan showed the need for further investigation for a mass it picked up. This is the reason the book was delayed, so my apologies.

People have to know about the organ retention scandal and about what it has done and continues to do to people. Like so many thousands, I still await answers to my questions – answers that may well lie just a few short miles away under lock and key in a warehouse off the M50 motorway. With the support of so many, and my requests for meetings with both Mary Harney and Brian Cowen, perhaps now we will get the answers we have been so long waiting for. God knows we've maintained a dignified campaign on behalf of our babies, children and loved ones for long enough. The time for action is now.

CHAPTER 1

Karina's Story:
Goodnight and God Bless, My Darling Glen

"The death of a baby is like a stone cast into the stillness of a quiet pool; the concentric ripples of despair sweep out in all directions, affecting many, many people." J DE FRAIN

This has been a very surreal and, at times, agonising book for me to write. After Glen's unexpected second funeral, which took place midway through writing and just weeks short of his nineteenth anniversary, it took me weeks to pick up where I had so suddenly left off. The wounds that were starting to heal had been ripped wide open and I honestly didn't know if I would have the emotional energy I knew it was going to take to finish what I had been so driven to start. I was now faced with the prospect of having to rewrite most of the book and, in particular, Glen's story; for in an instant, it had changed forever and I knew things would never be the same again.

This was the stuff horror films and urban legends are made of, but the awful truth was, I knew it was real. I had been here before. Unless you have been through the horror of unauthorised organ retention you will never truly understand the pain; but I am going to do my best to show you.

Many people in Ireland are today unaware they too could be part of what can only be described as one of Ireland's darkest recesses. A place nobody wants to go; an organisation nobody wants membership of. Sadly it's not a particularly exclusive club; it has many thousands of members in Ireland and many millions across the world. It has the potential for many more thousands in Ireland. Like most, I knew about it before I knew I was a member and by then my life had irrevocably changed.

I felt I had failed – as a mother – to protect my son from the grotesque and undignified way his tiny body had been violated and mutilated in death. Of course, retrospectively, I know there was nothing I could have done to prevent what happened from happening, for I was unaware of its occurrence until many years after it took place. However, it is a mother's primal instinct to protect and defend her children, both inside and outside her womb. The pain when she feels she fails is unbearable, unrelenting and unforgiving. It is something she learns to come to terms with; but it takes time – a lot of time – and a lot of soul searching. Eventually the raw grief passes; but you never forget the pain and, of course, you never forget your baby.

It is hard not to conjure up horrific images from what little you know and many nights are spent screaming in torment from nightmares. I spent so many nights waiting to escape the clutches of darkness. I still sleep with the bedroom door ajar; I don't like the dark. The nightmares remain, only now they are worse.

I recently had a nightmare where Glen was standing at the bedroom door. I was in that haze where you don't know whether you are awake or asleep, but I could clearly see him, or what was left of him. He had no eyes and there were gaping holes in his stomach, but there was no blood. The strange thing was that, although he was only a new baby, he could stand perfectly and could also talk. He repeated the same words three times before vanishing: *"Where's my brain and the rest of me, Mummy? Why did they do this?"* I bolted upright in the bed with perspiration and tears running down my face. It was so vivid.

I have fought with my instinct and intellect, battled with my emotions in what has been, on my part, a Trojan effort to face the pain head-on rather than allow the luxury of time to deal with it properly. It is difficult to write about such barbarity when you have just encountered it on an intensely personal basis for a third time – finding out his organs had been incinerated in 2001 and burying him twice (1990 and 2008).

When the pungent smell of the freshly dug earth from the grave still lingers in your nose, no matter the time or place. When the image of a ray of light bouncing off yet another of your child's brass coffin nameplates reflects the light in all its morning glory. Standing at that graveside on a cold winter's morning, just weeks ago, I felt numb. I didn't feel the cold; my numbness came from shock and disbelief that this could be happening all over again. It was the most unimaginably horrific *déjà vu* that any parent could ever go through. With silent tears streaming down my face, I kissed Glen's second casket and quietly told my son to go towards the light with his head held high, for He was waiting to welcome him home. It was time to rest; he had made a difference and he had an immortality most people will never have.

As those who loved him bade him farewell with the love and dignity he had battled so hard for, I was infused with a grief so deep that I was afraid to open its door fully, until this book was rewritten. I placed a personal effect into the grave and then walked away, trying not to look back. The rest of his immediate family also placed their own treasured possessions in the grave.

The irrational and illogical must be accorded their place for now, for there is no rationality and logic in death, nor is there a right or a wrong way to deal with grief.

I whispered to Glen to hold his head high as he soared towards the light, simply to make the impossible possible. Glen's brain and some other organs are still missing, so I knew he could never hold his head up straight.

I knew it was possible, though perhaps now not probable because of this book, that I may one day find them and return them to where they rightfully belong. This is the reason I refuse to etch his name on the tombstone while even the smallest hope remains. However slim it may be, hope is what keeps our hearts beating, for without it, we have nothing.

At this moment I am sitting in my home office with almost regimental self-discipline. Every word I type echoes in the perfectly silent room. The only sound I can hear is the constant ticking of a clock resonating around the room. In a strange way its constant beat is comforting, as is the precision with which my computer prompts me every half hour. For some reason I find it easier to write in complete silence, which is highly unusual for me. However, there is nothing normal about this, so I do not become analytical about my every move or behaviour. I have not been sleeping well and although physically tired, my mind is alert. It is so alert I cannot switch it off; during the night I read through post mortems and reports. My only focus is this book. I am like a sponge for knowledge and information, and at times I treat the exercise like a jigsaw. However, those who have completed complicated and intricate jigsaws, which challenge the mind, will know the horror of a missing piece. For now, this will be the easiest way for you to think of this scandal. The reality will be beyond comprehension at first; it was for me.

I am not foolish enough to think, for a minute, that I have escaped the grief that will come crashing into my world when this book goes (in fact it came crashing before the book was finished). I think that perhaps this is the reason it is taking what seems to be an incredibly long time to write. The fact that it is only six months since my last book was published does not register. A lifetime has passed since *Hear*

My Silence: Overcoming Depression was published to critically acclaimed reviews. Little did I know then the dark path on which life was to place me once again so soon, just as I was coming to terms with my depression.

Every so often, particularly when I find it hard to type the words, I look at one of two photographs strategically placed at either side of my computer and one, unframed, stuck to the end of my computer screen. This is the one that particularly drives me when I am stumbling; when I want to just run as far as I can possibly run from this macabre and nightmarish world in which I now exist among missing children's organs, adults' organs, blanked-out cheques and silence. It is an ultrasound scan printout, the only picture I have of my son alive, with his heart beating, his brain pulsating and his legs and arms poking through my distended stomach as he became enraptured with the excitement of being able to move his arms and legs and react to the sound of my voice and touch. I often smile at the memory, but my gaze always returns to the second picture. It is a photograph of Glen's recent casket – pristine white, with its gold nameplate glistening. I took it during the prayer service, *after* I put his photograph on top of it.

Glen wasn't some obscure and grossly – and deliberately – underestimated statistic. Glen was a beloved son, brother, grandson, nephew and cousin who was deeply loved and wanted from the moment we learned of his conception.

I thoroughly enjoyed the pregnancy and sailed into the second trimester. As I had previously had two miscarriages in the early stages of pregnancy, this was an important psychological milestone for us. I began to relax a little and even started buying baby clothes. I spent a long time preparing Karl, who was just two and a half, for the arrival of a baby brother or sister. He was very excited and as my stomach grew he would wake up every morning and say: "Baby come today?" My stomach seemed to be growing on almost a daily basis. I didn't remember being this big before at seven months. It was quite amazing.

My back, however, was struggling with the pressure of the extra weight and I had to start using crutches to get around. I suffered from sciatica at the time and really was in some discomfort. A decision was taken at the start of December to admit me to hospital for a week, for complete rest. Although the thought horrified me, I didn't put up much of a fight. After all, a week wasn't that long and I knew I would see Karl every day. I was quite organised for Christmas and as we were having Christmas dinner at my mother's I didn't have to worry too much about food shopping. Santa had been taken care of well in advance. I wasn't just organised because I was pregnant; I have always been a terror for picking things up for Christmas throughout the year.

The days passed quite quickly in the hospital and I spent the majority of my time reading and to my surprise, napping. Every day Karl asked if it was the day that baby was coming. I told him it was likely that Santa would come first. The excitement of Santa was enough to distract him. I was thankful that small children live only for the here and now!

The week passed and it was finally the day to go home. It was decided that I would have a scan before I went, to save me coming in again the following week. That's all it was; a routine scan. My stomach continued to grow rapidly and I mentioned it to my doctor. She said babies often grow at different rates and that I wasn't to worry. She said she would meet me when I went for my scan.

Late that morning I went to have my scan. I was looking forward to going home. Although my time in the hospital had passed quickly, it seemed I had been away from home a long time. I couldn't wait to be there to put Karl to bed, not to mention getting something that was horrifically calorific for dinner. Although the hospital food was good, it was no match for home cooking or, better still, the sinful delight of a takeaway meal. No wonder I had a smile on my face the whole way to the radiology department! True to her word, my doctor was waiting for me outside the door when I got there. She greeted me with a bright smile and said they were ready for me. The only thought I had walking into the scan room was that I was going home. The transition from brightness to darkness took a few seconds to adjust to, but no more than that.

My doctor stood by the monitor at the side of my bed, careful not to block my view of the screen. As the sonographer spread the cold, wet, familiar conductor gel on my stomach in preparation for the ultrasound, I grew very excited about seeing my baby. All thoughts of Chinese takeaway quickly left my head as I strained to see the first images appear on screen. I had asked for a photograph to bring home to Gerry and Karl, and indeed the rest of the family.

There it was! My baby's head! He was utterly recognisable on the screen in front of me. He was lying on his right side, so I was looking at a full view of his left profile. My eyes next went to his neck, and then to his arms, his stomach, and legs; one of which was poised midair, ready to strike. I was sorry I had told Gerry not to bother coming in until it was time for me to go after the scan. The image was so clear on the screen that I knew he would have loved to see it. I felt the week had been disruptive enough for him with me not at home, so I tried to keep further interruption to a minimum. The plan was to be in time to collect Karl from playschool. However, my mother was on standby, just in case we were running late for any reason.

It took a couple of minutes for me to register that the sonographer was still scanning me and my doctor had moved much closer to the screen. I was immediately conscious of a tension in the room and a change in the tone of their voices. The bright smiles gave way to furrowed brows and worried looks. As my doctor turned to face me, I closed my eyes. I didn't want to see her face or hear her words, but there was no escaping. "Karina," she said gently, "is Gerry on his way in?" I replied that he was and should be nearly there.

I remember this sick feeling rising from my stomach. I could feel bile rising in my throat and my head start to spin. I wanted to put my fingers in my ears. I wanted to wind the clock back, even just a few minutes. I wanted to be anywhere else except here. Was there no shutting this woman up? I closed my eyes and prayed that when I opened them I would realise this wasn't really happening after all. However, when I opened them, everything was exactly the same. I switched off; I have always had an innate ability to do this. Finally, she was like a goldfish; her mouth was moving, but I could no longer hear her words.

I knew I couldn't stay this way, so I began to sit up. I remember the sonographer wiping the gel off my stomach with a look of utter compassion. Everything was going in slow motion. The hustle and bustle of busy hospital life became silent for me. In auto-pilot, I walked back slowly. How could so much change in so little time? I was on my way home, my case packed, I was ready to walk out the door to go home; and now, in a matter of minutes, my whole world and that of my family had irrevocably changed.

I decided to ring my mother and broke down as soon as I heard her voice. She soothed me and told me Gerry had left for the hospital some time previously. I knew he was about to appear any minute, so I stayed on the phone to Mum. Gerry arrived a short time later and I told my mother I would keep her up to date and we arranged for her to collect Karl. I knew deep down that there was no way now that our lives were ever going to be the same again.

I fleetingly considered just walking out of the hospital and going home, but I knew this wasn't an option. Gerry paged my doctor and she told him she would be right with us. Although he remained calm for me, I could feel Gerry's fear penetrate the air. He put forth all the logical arguments, while I listened, knowing neither of us really believed what he was saying. Our doctor arrived, gave each of us a hug and led us to a room. She waited until we were both seated before she began to speak. I took a deep breath and, in an instant, decided that, whatever we were told, I was going home and, furthermore, so was my baby.

She gently explained that Glen was very poorly and that his chances of survival were minimal. She reassured us that should he survive they would do everything, including flying us to the UK. As she spoke to us, I could feel Glen kicking and at that moment I chose to believe the doctor was mistaken. As long as there was hope, I knew I could cope with it. I decided Glen was going to defy the doctors and beat all the odds. He had to; I needed him to. We needed him. He was so very wanted and so very much loved. Like all parents-to-be, we had so many hopes and dreams for him, but our greatest wish – that the baby be healthy – had been cruelly shattered and snatched from us. We felt it so unfair that we had come this far only to face losing him.

I knew I had to get out of the hospital and go home. I needed to bring Glen home where I could keep him safe. I knew that as long as he was with me, there was hope.

As Christmas approached, Karl's excitement grew and it was hard to get him to grasp that the baby was very poorly and may go to heaven instead of coming home. I don't really think he understood, as he still repeated the same question every morning: "Baby come today?"

Christmas was a very muted affair and my mother took care of everything. I didn't have the heart to put up decorations, but she said it wasn't fair on Karl, so she put up a beautiful tree. I knew that with each day that passed, the baby was either getting stronger or getting weaker; there was nothing to indicate which, as he was still kicking. Christmas came and went and still I clung to the hope that the doctors were wrong. However, on New Year's Eve, I didn't feel any movement so I rang the hospital and was asked to come in.

I delayed going in but knew I couldn't put it off forever, so eventually we went. The sonographer put the gel on and I prayed like I had never prayed before in my life. I pleaded with God not to take my baby because I wanted him too, no matter what was wrong with him. I felt the familiar sensation of the sensor rolling across my stomach, only this time; I averted my eyes from the screen. I willed him to kick, but there was no movement. The sonographer excused herself from the room and at that moment what little hope I had was extinguished.

The sonographer returned with a doctor. I knew what she was going to say before she opened her mouth. I didn't want to hear it, though, because that would make it real. I only heard her say: "I am so very sorry . . .". I was strangely calm as I sat up clumsily because of the size of my stomach. I looked at the screen; I looked at my stomach; I looked at the expression of compassion on the doctor's face; and finally, I turned to look at Gerry and broke down.

The sonographer and doctor tactfully left the room to give us some time on our own. Then the doctor brought us to a private area and explained what would happen next. It was agreed that they would induce me, but I refused to have it done until the following day. I wanted to bring Glen home one last time. I wanted to say goodbye at the same time as not ever wanting to. As we drove home, I remember looking out the car window at people revelling and bringing in the New Year and I wanted to scream at them to stop because my baby had just died.

I didn't sleep that night. So many things went through my head and the only thing I knew was that I didn't want to let him go. My will was so strong that the induction failed and it was decided to let nature take its course.

When Time Stood Still

I knew that I was now living on borrowed time, but every minute I had was precious for I could pretend that everything was going to be okay. We had to explain to Karl that the baby would not be coming home. I could see how confused he was and I wondered what was going through his little mind as he looked at my very swollen belly.

Mother Nature was stronger than I, however, and twelve days later, on 12th January, I went into labour spontaneously. The time I had been dreading for so long had finally come. It was time to give birth to the baby I had fought so hard to keep and who I knew had also fought so hard to make it. So close, yet it was not to be. The birth was swift and what I remember most about it is the silence. There was no cry, just silence; complete silence. My doctor broke the silence by telling us he was beautiful, with tears in her own eyes. In the distance I could hear the indignant yell of another new baby coming into the world.

I knew I was going to have to cram a lifetime of love into a few short hours. I knew I was going to have to say goodbye to the son I loved but would never know. I knew the end had come and I was powerless to prevent it. The doctor brought Glen to me wrapped in a blanket. She showed us his little hands and feet, his legs and arms and his beautiful face. I didn't see a dead baby; I saw my son. I was overcome with emotion and a pain that was so raw it was as if someone was twisting my heart. I lost track of everything as I absorbed every detail of my beautiful son. That was the moment when time stood still. As the tears fell I thought about all the things we would never do and I would never witness – first words, first teeth, first step, first day at school; so very many things.

I didn't sleep that night; I couldn't get the thought of Glen lying in a cold and dark mortuary out of my head. I wanted to go to him with a blanket. I also wrote him a letter and gathered keepsakes I wanted to put into his coffin. I wasn't sure what to expect when we went to the mortuary the following morning, as I had never been in one before. However, I need not have worried. Glen was in a Moses basket, which was on a table surrounded by flowers and two candles brightly burning. Now it was real; there was no pretending any more. My darling son was dead and I had only this brief time to say goodbye to him. As I gazed into the basket he looked as if he were sleeping. I remember thinking I would disturb him by lifting him out.

I sat down on a chair beside the basket and the nurse gently placed Glen in my arms. I was crying so hard, I was terrified I would drop him. One part of me wanted to make a mad dash out the door with him, but reality prevailed and I knew Glen would never come home. We spent a long time there, each of us taking turns to hold him; talk to him; tell him about his family who loved him, his big brother; sing to him; say goodbye to him with our hearts breaking. Even through the blankets, I could feel Glen was cold. I remember instinctively pulling them tighter around him to try to warm him up. We took photographs and the nurse took a photograph of me holding Glen alongside Gerry. It should have been a very different photograph; two proud parents with their new baby, all beaming. Instead the picture showed two heartbroken parents, their faces ravaged by the pain of grief, their eyes red from crying, both gazing down at their precious son who was dead and taking with him the death of their dream.

I don't know how long we were there, but it was a long time. I knew I only had this one chance to cram in all the love I had for him; I wanted him to know how very special he was and how very much he would be missed. I wanted him to know he would always be a part of our family. I held him tightly and took in every last detail. Eventually, Gerry persuaded me that it was time to go. I kissed Glen goodbye ever so gently and reluctantly handed him back to the nurse, telling her to look after him.

We made our way back home, each lost in thought. Gerry had tactfully put all the baby things away while I was in the hospital. My legs felt like lead as I walked and my head felt as if it were going to explode. I retreated into myself. I knew we were going to have to face a funeral and I knew that I would never see Glen again.

We arrived at the mortuary at 10.15 a.m. The priest said some prayers and then there was a minute's silence for personal prayers. After one final prayer, it was time to go and as I stood up I could feel my legs give from under me. I sat down again and tried to compose myself. When I felt ready to go, Gerry carried Glen's coffin to the car and we travelled to the cemetery with his tiny white coffin across our knees.

When we got to the cemetery, I clutched the coffin and begged Gerry not to take my son from me. He said that we had to let him go and that he was sure Glen was watching over us. He said we had to be strong and let him go. As Gerry handed the coffin over, I said my final goodbye. As the coffin was being lowered I just couldn't take any more and ran back to the car. I had no choice now but to accept that my darling son was gone.

The pain was quite physical and I didn't eat for the best part of a month after Glen's burial. My mother made me a plain tomato sandwich one day and put the plate in front of me. "You have another son to think of," she said, and something just clicked in my head. In time, life returned to some sense of normality, but at the least expected moments I would find myself crying.

When we discovered we were pregnant again we were both delighted and terrified. I was closely monitored during the pregnancy and gave birth to our daughter Sarah the day before Glen's second anniversary. It was a bittersweet moment when we heard her yell, and there wasn't a dry eye in the theatre; only this time, they were tears of joy. When everyone left and I was on my own, I looked out the window at the night sky. One star stood out from all the others as it brightly twinkled, lighting up all around it. "Glen's Star," I thought to myself. It was just after midnight. "Happy birthday, Glen," I said silently as I looked at his little sister sleeping peacefully, quite oblivious to the poignancy of the moment. This time we would leave the hospital with our baby.

I wanted Glen's short life to represent something positive, for I knew he had purpose. During my pregnancy I had so many personal questions about what to expect, but didn't really want to ask. For example, I didn't know what a dead baby looked like or what labour would be like. Would I be frightened of him? Would I bond with him? As it happened, I had no need to worry, I fell in love with him the moment I saw him, just as I had his brother.

This was before the advent of the internet as the tool of knowledge it is today. I decided to write the book I had needed but which didn't exist. *If It Happens to You: Miscarriage and Stillbirth – A Human Insight* was very well received and I felt I had given Glen immortality through it. The letters I received showed it had helped people and I knew that is what Glen would have wanted. Little did I know the nightmare that would engulf me time and time again some years later.

In 1999, the Bristol and Alder Hey scandals broke in the UK, where it became apparent that the organs of babies and children were being removed and retained for various reasons, including commercial. These scandals were quickly followed by the "cash for tissues" row. My immediate thought was for those poor parents and how they were going to cope. I began to think to myself and wondered if the same practice was going on in Irish hospitals – not for a moment believing it was. Things like that don't happen in modern-day Ireland.

I contacted the hospital Glen was born in and some time later my husband and I went in for a meeting. We were told that Glen's organs had been removed and retained without our consent. Furthermore, we were told that, some years previous to the meeting, they had been incinerated like clinical waste without informing us or giving us the opportunity to bury them with him. I left the hospital in shock and it took quite a while to get over emotionally, for the wounds that were healing had now been ripped wide open again. Once again, in time, they began to heal.

I have no fury; much of that left me the day I confronted the pathologist who performed my son's autopsy. When I looked him in the eyes and asked him about his own children, he was silent, averted his eyes and I got up and left the room without saying another word. I had intended to include a report here on a meeting that had been scheduled with the new Master and the same pathologist and the same social worker who had attended the one in 2001; but my hospitalisation meant this had to be rescheduled for a later date. However, I did manage to speak with Dr Gillian on his own and he went through all my questions with me, giving me as much time as I needed.

In September 2008, while researching this book, I decided, more out of curiosity than anything else, to make further enquiries about Glen. I think I just wanted confirmation in my own mind of what I had been told years ago. The letter I had received originally was destroyed when our house was gutted in a house fire in 2005, so I had nothing really to refer to if I wanted to refresh my memory. You cannot begin to imagine my shock when I received a letter confirming that there were sixty-two pieces of my son still at the hospital, with the offer to assist me reburying them with him. For the third time I had been thrown into this nightmare by chance.

This is something I will never understand. It is simply unbelievable and, of course, profoundly sad, that this could happen as common and acceptable ethical practice in modern-day Ireland.

I wrote directly to the Master as soon as I found out and built up a good rapport with him. I wrote to him a second time with a list of questions I had – some he was in a position to answer; some he was not as unbelievably no records existed. In my first letter I just wanted confirmation. In my second letter, I wanted answers. Dr Michael Geary's response is shown in full on pages 40-43.

Dr. Michael Geary
Master

The
Rotunda Hospital
DUBLIN
generations of care

7th November, 2008.

Ms. Karina Colgan,

Dear Ms. Colgan,

I refer to your letter dated 30th September 2008. I apologise for the delay in responding to you, however additional time was needed in order to address each of the questions raised in your letter.

The questions that you had asked in your letter have been dealt with individually as follows:

1. "Were any of my son's organs removed and retained without our consent?"

It was international practice at that time and the consent given for a post mortem was deemed to include the retention and removal of organs/tissues where required in order to make a diagnosis and determine cause of death.

2. "If so, what *exactly* was removed"

According to Hospital records the following organs and tissues were removed for careful examination to seek to establish the cause of death:
Lungs, heart, liver, spleen, kidneys, some glands (adrenal glands and thymus).
The brain was removed and retained for detailed examination.
Unfortunately, the records do not identify how many of the above organs and tissues were retained (other than the brain) or how many of those organs and tissues were put back in to the body.

3. "What were the organs, tissue samples and blocks that were removed?"

In relation to this question please refer to the letter dated 10th October 2008 that you received from the Information Management Department.

Founded 1745

not for prescription purposes

The Rotunda Hospital, Dublin 1. Tel 01 872 9005 Fax 01 873 0932
email: masterssecretary@rotunda.ie www.rotunda.ie

Accredited
ORGANISATION

3. Where were they incinerated

It is not clear where the incineration took place but it is most likely that it was either on the site of the Mater Hospital or Rotunda Hospital.

4. When they were incinerated and why?

As mentioned above it is not possible to state exactly when they were incinerated. This was the practice at the time in the early 1990s. I can understand that you would want to have been told this and afforded the opportunity of burying Glen's organs with his body. I am sorry that this was not the practice at the time and I am sorry that if revisiting this causes you distress.

5. What weight was Glen's brain with his spinal column – this was not recorded?

I have looked at the post-mortem report and there is no recorded weight for the brain and spinal column.

6. What if anything did further histological examination of the brain show?

It would appear that histological examination showed acute neuronal necrosis in the thalamus part of the brain. This is consistent with reduction in blood supply to the area which can lead to breakdown of the cellular structure of that particular tissue.

7. Whose decision was it to retain tissues and why?

This would have been the practice of the Pathology Department at the time.

8. How many organs have you got in the hospital now and why?

I am not at liberty to discuss what organs remain in the hospital pertaining to other babies. This is personal information pertaining to other babies and families. The Hospital has participated in the National Organ Retention Review and it is expected that the findings of this will be published over the next few months.

9. Has the hospital a patient liaison officer on the staff?

At the present time we do not have a patient liaison officer on staff. However the hospital is looking at the prospect of setting up a Patient Liaison Committee. It is hoped to make progress in this area in the coming months.

10. How do you ensure that a parent has informed consent when being asked to agree to a post-mortem?

The current practice at the Rotunda is that details of a post-mortem are discussed fully in advance with the parent/parents. Information leaflets are provided. The parent(s) have the opportunity to discuss the issues with the Bereavement Midwife in addition to the medical team. A consent form is signed and I believe that the current practice now in 2008 is consistent with a fully informed consent process.

11. What changes have been put into place in the hospital since the organ retention scandal broke to ensure that it doesn't happen again?

As mentioned in the previous letter we have a specific Bereavement Liaison Midwife working fulltime in this area. I believe that our information leaflets and consent process has greatly improved. In situations where there is need to retain organs we get the parents agreement/permission as to what exactly their wishes are with respect to future reburial or cremation of organs and whether the parent(s) wish to do this themselves or wish the hospital to arrange this.

12. What are they?

See 11 above.

13. Did you, as a hospital, co-operate with the Dunne and Madden Reports?

Yes.

14. On what grounds was the decision taken for the Rotunda not to provide pharmaceutical companies with pituitary glands?

I am unable to find any clear evidence as to what the thinking was at the time not to provide pituitary glands to pharmaceutical companies.

15. Finally, do you think there is an urgent need for Human Tissue Act legislation to be introduced without further delay given it took just nine months to enact after the scandal broke in Alder, UK?

I do not wish to get into a personal opinion here but I do know that the HSE and Department of Health are looking at this matter seriously.

16. "According to the Madden Report in 1995, it was a recommendation that all organs and not disposed of within 12 months should be incinerated. They recommended a public information campaign – did the Rotunda take part in such a campaign? Is this common practice now in the hospital?"

The Madden Report in 2005 recommends that if after 12 months organs remained unclaimed they must be disposed of respectfully by the Hospital either by burial in approved Hospital plot or crematorium. I can confirm that the Rotunda Hospital carried out a public information campaign in 2000.

17. "What other changes the Rotunda as a result of the Organ Retention Scandal has made and do you now have a bereavement liaison nurse on the staff?"

Yes, the Rotunda Hospital currently has a Bereavement Liaison Nurse on staff.

I hope the above is of assistance to you and answers your queries in relation to this matter.

Should you have any queries please do not hesitate to contact me on

Yours sincerely,

Dr. Michael Geary
Master

Glen's maternal grandmother, Babbis, sketched the picture of Glen that is at the beginning of this chapter, while sitting by his side in the morgue in 1990; she says it was the hardest picture she ever drew. (It is very important in the hospital to take as many photos as you want to. Ask a nurse to take a family photo also. It is also a good idea to take your baby's hand and footprints: bring in a pot of poster paint and white cardboard. You only have one chance to do this.) Babbis is what my mother is called by everyone – young and old alike. It was a name that Karl bestowed on her when he could barely talk and it just stuck, to the extent that I have had neighbours ask me what her real name is so they can send her Christmas cards. As you will see from her account below, the death of a loved one affects a whole family.

Goodbye *"Little One"*

The news my daughter, Karina, and son-in-law, Gerry, greeted me with that summer afternoon brought a smile to my face as big as the smiles they wore; a new grandchild was on the way, a sibling for grandson, Karl. Already my mind turned towards the traditional task of grandmothers as I contemplated the merits of various knitting yarns.

Karina kept well even though she was on crutches throughout the second semester due to sciatica and we all looked forward to the new arrival, who was due late winter/early spring. Unlike those around me, I was of the opinion that when Mother Nature was ready, out would pop baby, but it didn't do much to allay their excitement. Christmas was just around the corner when Karina was due for another routine check-up in the antenatal clinic. This time she was admitted for a week for bed rest and Gerry and I looked after Karl. On the day of her discharge, when Karina rang at noon I expected to hear at what time she would be free for lunch; instead, I heard her sobbing, barely coherent. She told me that, just as she was about to leave the hospital with a good report on her condition, it was decided she should have a routine scan and save having to come back at a later date.

The doctors revealed that the scan had shown a problem and asked Karina if she could have her husband call to the hospital . . . they were told that the baby was dying and that there was nothing they could do to save him.

So kind and helpful in all areas, the medical staff at the hospital would have flown Karina anywhere if they thought Glen had any chance at all. He was alive, and although his movements slowed down, he made enough movement to make his presence felt. Close enough to place a hand on his Mummy's tummy, although they couldn't play their game any more where Karina would place a ball of wool on her stomach and he would kick it off again! He may have been stillborn, but he *was* – he lived.

It was such a sad Christmas. Glen still held on and fought as hard as he could. However, on New Year's Eve, Karina felt no movement and put off going into the hospital as long as she could. They could not detect a heartbeat. *Our little fighter had lost his battle for life.*

They wanted to induce the birth there and then but met with fierce resistance from Karina, who felt that while he was in the womb she still had him. Knowing that to see him was to say goodbye was certainly something she found so hard to accept. She hung on another two weeks before Mother Nature decided it was time to let him go.

Such a sad time it was when, on 12th January, Glen arrived. Karina gave birth and we spent some time with him. Gerry held him and sang a song he had composed especially for him, after which he placed his favourite guitar strap next to Glen; this they later buried with him, as he was laid to rest next to his great grandparents, Samuel and Christina Turner. Karina didn't want him to be alone.

As I tearfully gazed down at the tiny little guy I held gently in my arms, it was hard to imagine that someone so small could have made such a big impact on those close to him. As we know now, he was to have a much greater impact on people in the future. His eyes were open and appeared to be gazing into my face, but Glen would never see. To me, he looked beautiful and perfect, but Glen had died in the womb two weeks previously. This was the only time I would ever hold him. Instinctively trying to warm him, I wrapped my arms more firmly around him.

This overwhelming sadness was in such contrast to the joy I had felt as I awaited his arrival. That evening I drove home, my eyes filling with tears as I thought of the knitting I would otherwise have done. Now I set about making a little outfit to bury Glen in. It was, in fact, a little white cotton lace-trimmed shroud with a matching bonnet.

A couple of days later, I went into the chapel of rest to say a final goodbye to Glen. As I gazed down at him, the little white cotton garment was gently laid over him and a big yellow flower touched his cheek. He looked such a sweet little baby lying there and all the might-have-beens were rushing through my mind, but this was it, this was all we would ever know of Glen. I took a pencil out of my bag and sketched him.

In his brief life – all of it lived in the womb – he was to make an impact on more people than most adults ever achieve. Short as his little life was, he didn't live, or die, in vain. It was Glen's brief life which saw his mother publish her first book, *If it Happens to You: Miscarriage and Stillbirth – A Human Insight*. This brought understanding and comfort to many who were touched by this subject.

Now, with the publication of this fourth book, he is part of the pursuit of justice by people for their loved ones, who deserved dignity not accorded to them.

You were, Glen, you were; you lived, and many thousands will know your name, and your story.

"With Christ which is far better"
PHILIPPIANS: 1:23

Glen's Song

I can't believe what we heard tonight,
Our unborn child may never see the light,
With six months gone and only three to go,
There's something wrong the doctors can't control.
My wife went in with just back pain,
Now there's so much more, they say we're not to blame,
At thirty weeks they'll do what they can do,
But our baby's getting sicker and the odds are
  getting few.

I can't believe what the doctors say,
"Sorry, there's no cure, just hope and pray,
Take your wife home; come back for weekly tests,
It's hard we know, try and see she rests."
This Christmas time's so hard to bear,
With our two-year-old son we try and share,
We feel so helpless, we hold on tight,
Please God our baby's strong enough to fight.

I can't believe what we heard today,
"The news is bad; your baby's passed away,
There is no heartbeat or movement in the womb,
We'll try some pills to bring on labour soon."
Two weeks have passed and it's so unreal,
Our hearts are breaking, such pain we feel.
The pills have failed and Mother Nature's slow,
My wife can't bear to let our baby go.

I can't believe what I saw today,
My wife gave birth, and they took our son away.
After so much pain, she was denied her wish;
He never got the chance to cry or kick,
We held him close and I tried to sing,
How much we loved and needed him.
Passed exit sign through an entrance door,
Our baby's coming home no more.

He had his mother's eyes and his father's mouth,
But he'll never see, or taste, or shout.
His grandmother's nose without a doubt,
Hands small and perfect but they'll never reach out.

I can't explain how I felt today,
As we laid our child beneath the clay.
A time to part, a farewell touch,
Our little Glen to God we trust.

In Heaven now our angel sings,
We live each day and think of him.
Through photographs and nightmare dreams,
Of all that was and could have been.

© GERRY COLGAN *Dec 1989–Jan 1990*

Author's note: Glen was not recognised in the "Madden Report"
because he did not fall within the limited age bracket imposed on the
Madden Inquiry.

CHAPTER 2

A Scandal Breaks in Ireland

"Know where to find the information and how to use it."

EINSTEIN

The opening quote to this chapter wasn't randomly chosen; it was carefully searched for and found. I chose it primarily because of its unintentional irony and its aptness to the organ retention scandal, which has betrayed the trust of people in Ireland.

Floods, fires, missing documents, buried organs, blacked-out pages, unpublished files, missing brains, missing organs, missing records, sale of pituitary glands, mutilation of deceased babies, toddlers, teenagers and adults, inaction, silence – this is the stark reality of the organ retention scandal in Ireland, which came to light in 1999. And so began my journey into the deep dark annals of what will in time surely be referred to as a dark period in Irish history, Irish medical ethics and indeed Irish politics.

Worldwide

Stealing, selling or harvesting body parts or organs without consent is a criminal offence across the world and as such is banned. Thus far, not one person has been held accountable

49

or questioned about money exchanging hands in Ireland (Madden Report 8.1, page 90).

So unethical is the practice deemed to be that China finally gave in to mounting pressure from around the world to discontinue its alleged practice of using the organs of executed people for transplantation. It banned the sale of any body part in 2006 and more recently adopted the policy that only blood relatives of the executed may have their organs.

However, demand for organs around the globe far outstrips supply and there are some who cannot resist the lure of big bucks that can be made from taking and selling organs without consent. The sentencing of Michael Mastromarino by a Philadelphia court in October 2008 for 25–58 years saw justice executed for his victims, who famously included veteran British broadcaster Alistair Cooke, who died in New York in 2004 aged ninety-five. It mattered not to Mastromarino that Cooke was riddled with cancer. His infected organs were harvested and his death certificate altered to make the man appear years younger than he was at the time of his death.

Mastromarino, who owned a biomedical facility in New Jersey, pleaded guilty to abusing corpses and forgery, among other allegations. This sentence will run concurrent with another 18–54-year sentence, which was handed down by a New York court for the same offences. Mastromarino worked in conjunction with Philadelphia-based undertakers Louis and Gerald Garzone, who are said to have sold at least 244 corpses to Mastromarino. The brothers were sentenced to 8–20 years.

Scandals have also raged in other countries, such as India (Dr Amit Kumar, 2008); South Africa (2001–2003);

UK (Dick van Velzen, a Dutch pathologist at Alder Hey, Liverpool, 1988–1994) and Ireland (nationally 1970–2000).

According to Parents for Justice, organ retention has been happening in Ireland since they started to do post mortems. Unfortunately not even coroners Denis Cusack or Brian Farrell could tell me when the first recorded post mortem took place in Ireland, but you can read about the history of post mortems in Chapter 10 (they go back further than you think). The dates above were just agreed on to keep the timeframe of the Inquiry a bit tighter. However, the Minister said that if there were any queries prior to 1970, they would also be included in the Inquiry process. This is one of the reasons why PFJ are sure that there are many thousands of families in Ireland at this time who just do not realise that they are potentially involved in this national scandal.

I am aware that horror stories have the potential to affect genuine and regulated organ donation carried out to give the precious gift of life or provide for medical research whether by cadaveric or living organ donations. So much so, I spent a long time talking to Mark Murphy, CEO of the Irish Kidney Association, about the scandal and the impact the aftermath had on the association. (Again you may read about kidney donation and his interview in Chapter 10.) However, these "horror stories" are *not* "stories"; they are reported from actual events that have happened to real people in Ireland up until recently. I know; I happen to be one of them.

The organ retention scandal broke in Ireland after news of the scandals at Bristol and Alder Hey Hospitals started making the national news in the UK in 1998. The scandal at Alder Hey was uncovered only after a chance remark made by heart specialist Professor Robert Anderson was picked up by the media. Anderson had revealed at the inquiry into the Bristol scandal that Alder Hey had a store of children's hearts. Indeed, as the official inquiry later showed, there were 2,000 unauthorised organs stored at the hospital without consent, including whole heads and bodies.

The organ retention scandal first broke in Ireland in the media in September 1999 but did not receive too much attention. However, when the scandal broke in Alder Hey in Liverpool in December 1999, it was brought to the attention of the public in Ireland by the media (see Charlotte's story in Chapter 3).

Ireland

Many of the families affected by the organ retention scandal here have said that they *would* have given permission, if this permission had been sought in an open and transparent manner, for the retention of some organs, depending on the use they were required for, had they been given the option of informed consent. However, these families were denied any comfort they may have received if they had been allowed to freely choose to donate organs or tissues if they had been needed for the good of future generations.

However, all families affected have stated that they never would have given permission for any of their children's or loved ones' organs to be *sold* for commercial purposes. Likewise, they would never have given permission for organs to be retained and then be left on a hospital shelf for years or to be incinerated like clinical waste.

The national organisation Parents for Justice (PFJ), was set up in 1999 by four parents soon after the scandal broke in the media to deal with the thousands of enquiries from other affected parents.

I have been a member since 2000. Hard as it is to believe, PFJ had to vacate its offices in Usher's Quay, Dublin in March 2008 because its funding was withdrawn by the Health Service Executive (HSE). Equally unbelievable is that funding to provide helplines and counselling for affected parents was also withdrawn, leaving many parents without recourse to any kind of counselling unless they paid for it themselves; some are not in a position to do so. You can read more about Parents for Justice in Chapter 4.

For the purpose of this book I wrote to the CEO of the HSE, Professor Brendan Drumm, about the decision to withdraw funding, but did not receive the courtesy of a reply from him. So much for a man who purports his door is "always open". PFJ also wrote to him to request a meeting last year and are still awaiting one.

Even with their office, helpline, and counselling services closed down, PFJ continues to offer help and advice from volunteers' own homes, funded entirely at their own expense. "We will not give up until we have the answers we have been demanding for over a decade now," says Charlotte Yeates, "no matter what it takes."

Chronology of Events

> *"I am afraid we must make the world honest before we can honestly say to our children that honesty is the best policy."*
>
> GEORGE BERNARD SHAW

It is now a decade since the organ retention scandal first broke in Ireland. Some people are vaguely aware of its existence, while others have little comprehension of it at all. In the coming pages I am going to take you through the scandal and give you an idea how many thousands of Irish people have been affected by it and, perhaps more importantly, are still to be affected by it after reading this book.

- 1998: Investigation into cardiac surgery practice on children at the Bristol Royal Infirmary in England.

- 11th February 1999: Detailed account on *UTV News* at 10 p.m. that children's hearts had been retained following post mortems.

- 12th February 1999: Our Lady's Hospital, Crumlin contacted by one distressed parent asking what the procedure was following a child's death from heart disease.

- 16th April 1999: Cardiologist admitted heart and lungs were removed, retained and disposed of following post mortem in Our Lady's Hospital without the consent or knowledge of parents. Further information in writing was sought by this mother.

- May 1999: Parents attended a meeting with CEO and Consultant Pathologist in Our Lady's Hospital to lodge a formal complaint. Parents said that if the practice was not stopped immediately they would make this information public. CEO advised the parents that there were *ninety-eight sets of human organs in storage at the hospital at that time*. The parents asked for an assurance that the families of the ninety-eight children involved would be contacted and told that their children's organs were still in storage in the hospital. The hospital refused.

- May 1999: The parents received a confirmation letter from the hospital, which included *a warning not to divulge this information to other parents* for "fear of causing upset to them".

- May 1999: Not satisfied with this, the parents wrote to then Minister for Health, Mr Brian Cowen, to make him aware of this practice in Ireland. They received a short letter in June saying "the matter would be brought to the attention of Minister Cowen in due course".

- May–August 1999: A second letter to Minister Brian Cowen followed and another similar reply was received from his office. *There was no contact from the Minister himself* to parents about this national scandal. Several visits were made to Our Lady's Hospital by an anxious mother to discuss consent forms for post mortems and she attended a meeting with the Bereavement Group in the hospital. The hospital then took the decision *not* to tell the ninety-eight families that their children's organs were still stored in the hospital.

- September 1999: An Irish Sunday newspaper printed a story about the organs of a small child being retained in Our Lady's Hospital. Apparently the consultant pathologist spoke to the reporter and confirmed a story that the journalist had heard about this case. The pathologist did not tell the parents that he had done this and the parents were shocked to read their daughter's story in a national paper (albeit that there were no names mentioned) without warning.

- September 1999: The following Sunday, after a lengthy discussion with the reporter, the mother's own story appeared in the paper. The mother was surprised that she had not had any response from other families whose children had died and had post mortems in Our Lady's Hospital, despite the fact that she had left her contact details with the hospital and asked them to forward them on to any other parents who might want to contact her.

- December 1999: Stories began to break in the media about Alder Hey Children's Hospital in Liverpool removing and retaining children's organs without consent.

- 5th December 1999: Three sets of parents in Ireland met for the first time and the mothers decided to establish Parents For Justice. They were joined the following week by another mother from Cork. They all had the same goal – a support group for parents whose children's organs were retained in Our Lady's. Little did they know how much their association was about to escalate.

- 10th December 1999: Two of these women appeared on *The Late Late Show* to speak about their experiences. Following the programme, parents wanting to know how to make enquiries inundated the show with phone calls. It very quickly became apparent that adults as well as children were involved in this scandal and that it was "best international practice" in hospitals and institutions all over Ireland.

- 15th December 1999: A meeting was finally held by PFJ with Minister Brian Cowen and Department of Health officials. PFJ demanded that an impartial public inquiry be established to find out exactly what had happened and to make sure it never happened again. Another meeting was held on 19th December 1999 to request that human tissue legislation be enacted as a matter of urgency.

- January 2000: Minister Micheál Martin replaced Minister Brian Cowen as Health Minister and there was real hope that something would be done at last and that answers would be forthcoming.

- 9th February 2000: During the first meeting with Minister Martin, he undertook to establish an Inquiry into Post Mortem Practices in the State. PFJ repeated their demand for the introduction of human tissue legislation to ensure that no other family would find themselves in the same position ever again. This issue had first been raised with Minister Brian Cowen on 19th December 1999. The exact nature of the Inquiry was to be decided upon, but the parents were assured that they would receive the answers they so desperately wanted. As you will read throughout this book, this was not the case at all.

- September 2000: Following numerous meetings with the Minister for Health and Department officials and following written and verbal assurances from the Minister given to members of Parents for Justice at a public meeting, members voted to co-operate with the proposed two-tier Inquiry to be set up *on the basis that the first part would be in private and the second part would have statutory powers*. The report from the first part was to go before the Joint Oireachtas Committee on Health and Children and they were to decide the nature of the second part (this was included in the "Memorandum on Procedures of the Post Mortem Inquiry", which was a legal document). However, this never happened. *The Joint Oireachtas Committee on Health and Children have never seen the report and therefore never got to make a decision about the second phase of the Post Mortem Inquiry*. This inquiry was to be cost-effective and expeditious.

- Late 2000: Ms Anne Dunne SC was appointed to chair the Post Mortem Inquiry.

- February 2001: Public notices were published setting out the terms of reference for the inquiry and seeking submissions.

- Early March 2001: The Post Mortem Inquiry team commenced its work in Dublin. Ms Dunne's "Interpretation of the Terms of Reference" was published with an undertaking to produce a report to the Minister for Health within eighteen months and not the six months that was included in the terms of reference in February.

- Late March 2001–October 2001: The inquiry began to hold oral interviews with some of the families involved. However, the four parents who had first brought this matter to the attention of the Government and the general public were not invited in for oral submissions, despite having handed in written submissions at the very onset of the inquiry process. Only one of these parents gave an oral submission and that was at her request because she was terminally ill with cancer.

- October 2002: Still no sign of the expected report from Ms Dunne. Numerous requests from PFJ for a progress report were ignored by the Minister for Health. After missing two of her own deadlines and with pressure mounting, Anne Dunne finally produced a progress report. PFJ and its members requested several times that Minister Micheál Martin place the private inquiry on the statutory footing he had promised. He refused. At this stage the inquiry had cost the taxpayer around €5 million.

- Late in October 2002 the Dunne Inquiry produced a progress report. It was evident that the inquiry team was not enjoying the complete co-operation of the medical profession that Minister Martin had been so certain would be forthcoming and, after much deliberation among members, PFJ decided to withdraw co-operation in October 2002.

- October 2002–December 2004: The Dunne Inquiry missed four more of its own deadlines to produce a report. Ms Dunne was then instructed to narrow her terms of reference and to concentrate on just *three Dublin hospitals* – one maternity and two children's hospitals – and to *ignore the remaining hospitals* in the country that had performed post mortems (twenty-six in total). Her initial remit had been to investigate every hospital in Ireland where post mortems were carried out. Anne Dunne had already done quite a lot of investigation into the various other hospitals before she was told to concentrate on just the three hospitals in Dublin. (You may read more about the hospitals in Chapter 10.)

- September 2004: Minister Micheál Martin was replaced by Ms Mary Harney as Minister for Health; Micheál Martin was appointed Minister for Trade, Enterprise and Employment.

- December 2004: Minister Harney announced that she was going to close down the Dunne Inquiry into post mortem practices in March 2005, completely disregarding phase 2, *which had been promised verbally and in writing by her predecessor.* As Health Minister, she had the right to do this, even if it was ethically questionable and overruled her predecessor's decision.

- 31st March 2005: Minister Mary Harney closed down the Dunne Inquiry. On that date Ms Anne Dunne delivered fifty-four bankers' boxes of documents, which included her report, to Minister Mary Harney. Ms Dunne's report has *never been published* on instructions of the then Attorney-General, Mr Ruairi Brady.

- May 2005: Minister Mary Harney appointed Dr Deirdre Madden to produce a report based on the contents of these fifty-four boxes. Dr Madden's terms of reference were very narrow and restricted her to making *recommendations only and not findings.*

- December 2005: The Madden Report was presented to the Minister for Health. Consisting of just 143 pages, it was based on the report that was included in the contents of the fifty-four boxes of documents delivered to Minister Harney when she closed down the Post Mortem Inquiry (Dunne Report) on 31st March 2005.

- January 2006: The Madden Report was made public. This report did *not* contain any findings from the past, only recommendations for the future as per her terms of reference (fifty of them in total). (The recommendations are listed at the end of Chapter 6.)

One of the recommendations of the Madden Report was to establish a working group, chaired by Dr Madden herself. At the request of Dr Madden, the Group comprised members from a number of associations and a range of disciplines. Two members of Parents for Justice, Charlotte Yeates and Breda Butler, were on the committee. They elected to put themselves forward because they wanted to see and hear what was going on and being discussed. "At the end of the day, let's face it: Deirdre Madden did what she was asked to do," said Yeates. "If there was going to be a working group then we wanted to be sure we had input into it. There was a lot of talking being done, but we felt much of it was about inconsequential stuff. We don't believe anything substantive came from it. Although a report was published in 2006, we are of the opinion that very little has been carried out or enacted since then. Just like with the Madden Report itself."

- August 2006: PFJ received an edited version of Ms Anne Dunne's report under the Freedom of Information Act (FOI). (You may read more about FOI at www.foi.gov.ie.) This version, which is in the possession of the author of this book, did not contain any findings either and many of the passages were blacked out.

- January 2007: PFJ made a submission to the Public Accounts Committee (PAC) re the cost of the Dunne Inquiry.

- May and August 2007: Truth and Reconciliation Forums were held by PFJ in Dublin Castle and in the Silver Springs Hotel in Cork, to allow parents to speak about their experiences because the Government would not allow them to. They were chaired by the same Ms Michaela Willis who later went on to carry out the Independent Audit of Human Organs in Irish Hospitals for the HSE (we are now awaiting the report of same).

- 14th February 2008: Following an FOI request by PFJ, they received another version of Ms Anne Dunne's report. This version included twenty-seven extra pages, which included the elusive "findings" by Ms Dunne. These findings were made public, and were very upsetting for families all over Ireland. Some of the information indicated that medical individuals may have benefited financially from the deaths of children and loved ones. This information was elicited from the FOI documents that PFJ had requested from all the hospitals and health boards who had submitted documents to the Post Mortem Inquiry. A sample of these documents appear in this book, including cheque stubs and invoices, in Chapter 8.

This new information also showed that sand, paper and/or cotton wool was placed inside the bodies of dead children after their organs had been removed. The information about the sand was actually one of Anne Dunne's findings in the second version of her report obtained in February 2008; page 33, 159:

"Because of the removal and retention of organs at post mortem examination, the body weight may differ after the examination and it is necessary to counteract this difficulty where babies and small children are concerned, by placing sand in the head and tow as packing material in the body. Because babies and small children are likely to be handled greater care in reconstruction is required."

- March 2008: The Joint Oireachtas Committee on Health and Children asked Minister Harney why their committee was never afforded the opportunity to see this report. Again, the Minister stated that it was on advice from the Attorney-General at the time, Ruairi Brady. Harney refused, however, to allow the committee to see the letter from him stating this.

- February/March 2008: Paul Gallagher, the present Attorney-General, also refused to meet with the Joint Committee on Health and Children to discuss this matter, saying he wasn't going to go against his predecessor.

There can be little doubt that the information contained in the fifty-four boxes may answer many of the questions people are asking. However, it may also turn up some unexpected information that *certain individuals wish it did not*. There is a written guarantee in place from Ms Harney that nothing will happen to these boxes and their contents.

Such was their desperation that at one point the directors and administrator of PFJ offered to be locked in the warehouse with the boxes so they could go through them. Each time they made this request – and there have been many – the Minister has refused them access. Ms Harney has stated "natural justice" as one of the reasons why she will not allow them access.

It is "natural" the Government wants "justice", I suppose, given the information we can only assume that those fifty-four boxes contain . . .

CHAPTER 3

Charlotte's Story:
The Brightest Star

*"Of all the rights of women,
the greatest is to be a mother."*
LIN YÜ-TANG

*Lorraine Yeates was born to
Charlotte and John Yeates and
had a beautiful big sister,
Nicola, aged three-and-a-half,
to help Mum look after her.
Charlotte was going to attend her routine post-natal
check up, and her father was going to mind Lorraine for
her. All of a sudden, Lorraine stopped breathing.
Charlotte takes up the story . . .*

We took her and shook her and she came back to normal.
I can tell you, I got the fright of my life and so did my
poor father.

67

I went straight to the baby clinic in the Coombe only to be told it was closed and to come back the next morning. It was 1.30 p.m. I refused to go and said I wanted my baby checked because I knew something was wrong. I rang my husband John, who came in to sit with me while we waited, and waited, and waited to see a doctor. Finally, a nurse took Lorraine from me and left the room.

A doctor came to see us at 6.00 p.m. and explained that Lorraine had been taken for an x-ray, as they thought she had pneumonia. In a way I was relieved because at least I knew what was wrong with her now. We left later that night, secure in the knowledge that Lorraine would soon be better. I rang the hospital that night to check how she was doing, only to be asked if Lorraine had been baptised. Utter panic set in at that stage. When I said no, the nurse said they would have a priest in the next morning to baptise her. So our little angel was baptised inside an incubator in the baby unit in the Coombe hospital. She was too sick to be taken out of it even for the ceremony.

The next morning we went to the hospital first thing and we left Nicola outside the door of the room Lorraine was in, but soon afterwards a man came in holding Nicola in his arms. He was explaining what all the machinery did and why it made the noises it did; he reassured Nicola a lot. We found out that he was actually Lorraine's cardiologist.

Lorraine remained in the Coombe for five days before being transferred to Our Lady's where, the day before Christmas Eve, it was diagnosed that Lorraine's heart was malformed and pointed in the wrong direction. It wasn't exactly the Christmas news we wanted to hear, but we decided then and there that we would just get on with it.

Lorraine had heart surgery the day before St Patrick's Day and finally came home to us on Good Friday; we were overjoyed and had a big family party. John and I were like two nervous wrecks, each of us taking turns in the beginning to see if we could hear her breathing. She was fine, though, and went back to the hospital for regular visits.

When she was two-and-a-half, Lorraine had open-heart surgery. Before the surgery they tried to get her to a certain height and weight, which they achieved, to a point. After surgery, the cardiologist came up to us, and I will never forget his words: "Enjoy every day with her." From that moment on, that's exactly what we decided to do. Yes, she could drop dead at any minute, but that wasn't going to mean she wasn't going to have a normal life. She had her own little circle of friends on the road and was almost glued to her dog Toby – they were inseparable. Although Lorraine couldn't walk very far or very fast, it was as if Toby instinctively knew this and used to just trot beside her. After she died, Toby was bereft; it took him a long time to realise she wasn't coming home to him again.

Lorraine was a real "Mammy's girl"; I think one of the reasons for this is that we spent so much time together in hospital. She never complained once about all she went through and, although a quiet child, she always had a smile ready for people and was a very kind and considerate little girl.

"Bosco" the puppet was Lorraine's favourite television programme and she would watch him for countless hours. I don't think she ever missed an episode. She was quite happy curled up with Toby, munching her way through custard cream biscuits! She loved Ladybird books and, believe it or not, Irish. My father had purchased a set of Irish cassette tapes and Lorraine was the only one interested in them, so the two of them would spend hours learning Irish together and she really enjoyed it.

Lorraine was a "home bird" and was quite content to stay at home with the family, Toby, her book and, of course, her hero, Bosco. Her little circle of friends, who all lived on our road, were very protective of her and were devastated when she passed away – although, in all the pain and suffering, just after Lorraine died, her little pal Erica came across to ask me firstly if they had custard creams in heaven, because they were Lorraine's favourite, and secondly, could she have her swing? It was a good example of how children live only for the here and now.

The week before she died, I went to hand her tricycle to her and the handlebars came off. "Don't worry," I said, "Daddy will fix it when he gets home."

"He doesn't need to, Mammy. I won't be needing it again," she said.

That was on the Saturday and she died on the Tuesday. I believe she knew the end was drawing near, but none of us did.

The weekend before she died, we all enjoyed a family day to Holyhead; she used to love going on the ferry and could never sleep with the excitement the night before.

There was nothing to indicate she was getting any sicker, so we treated her as normally as we possibly could.

Her godmother made her a beautiful new dress that weekend and she wanted to wear it to school on the Monday. I explained that she had to wear her school uniform. With that, she turned to me and she said, "Mummy, I will wear that dress on Wednesday." The next day was 18th June and Sports Day at school. Although Lorraine couldn't partake in anything, she donned her tracksuit and over we went to watch. It finished about 1.00 p.m. and she fretted to come home with me, so the teacher said that was fine. Nicola was in the yard beside her and allowed her to open the window and give her a kiss, "Love you, Nicki," she said, and with that we made our way home. Those were the last words Nicola ever heard her little sister say.

I was carrying Lorraine and her bag and some of Nicola's things as well, so I asked Lorraine if she could walk even a few steps. I turned the corner and then saw her turn the corner. She didn't look well, so I dropped everything and rushed up to her, just in time to hear her say "Oh Mammy" and catch her before she hit the ground. I carried her to the nearest house and asked for a lift to the hospital. The whole way there, I gave her mouth-to-mouth resuscitation. As soon as we got into the clinic they took her straight from me; they knew she had had a massive heart attack and they ran with her in their arms. This was like a nightmare to me.

That evening at 9.00 p.m. she had another massive heart attack and was pronounced dead at 9.45 p.m., aged five years, eight months and eighteen days. I would like to say the hospital did everything they could to save her life that day; even though I was to battle with them later, I know that while Lorraine was alive, she received the very best of care from all in the hospital, particularly her cardiologist and the eminent heart surgeon who performed her surgeries.

Our precious little girl was in the hospital for less than ten hours. The staff rang our local priest and he said prayers at the hospital. We were then told she had to have a post mortem; they said it was a coroner's post mortem (we subsequently found out that it was not) and that they did not need our permission to carry it out. We were also told we actually had no say in the matter and it was only an act of courtesy that they were telling us at all. We didn't know any differently at the time. I actually rang the hospital later on to ask if any of Lorraine's organs may be of use to another child and was told "no", because she had been on medication all her life.

On Wednesday, Lorraine was buried in her new dress; she got to wear it, just like she said she would, after all. The funeral was everything you would expect a child's funeral to be and, even though you try to be thankful you had her for what little time you did and try to make it a celebration of her life, your heart is breaking.

I had a dream four nights after she died that somehow she was in the room on a gurney. I lifted her nightdress and the scar she had running down her chest from the operations had vanished. Out of nowhere decipherable, a voice said to me: "She has no blemishes now."

"Is this heaven?" I asked.

"Yes, it is."

Then everything vanished as quickly as it had appeared.

I was forever setting the dinner table for four, or seeing someone in the street who looked like Lorraine. It took a long time to stop doing this. I was away with a friend a couple of years ago and I was feeling so down one day. I just couldn't get Lorraine out of my head; I just wanted to go home. However, my friend frantically beckoned me over to a street stall that sold crystals. As I was standing on the other side, I couldn't see what his excitement was all about. Fair enough, the crystals were nice, but that's as far as it went. He pushed me around the other side and it was as if a miracle had happened – there, looking at me, was a crystal with the name "Lorraine" on it. The craftsman offered to make us a new one, but we knew this was the one I was meant to have.

Time stood still. This wasn't a smell, this was something tangible, and I knew at that moment that Lorraine was with me, willing me on, just as she always will be. When times get tough or I feel like giving up, all I have to do is remember my beautiful little angel and I know why it's so very important to fight for justice for her and all the other children and adults who have been affected by the organ retention scandal in Ireland and to make sure that this doesn't happen to another child or adult in this country. *Wouldn't you do the same if she were your little girl?*

CHAPTER 4

Parents for Justice:
An Intimate History

"The higher the wall, the higher we'll jump."
CHARLOTTE YEATES

Parents for Justice is the national organisation which represents the families of those whose organs were removed, retained, disposed of and in some cases sold to pharmaceutical companies without the consent or knowledge of the parents or next of kin. It is a nationwide organisation, representing thousands of members.

When the founders first met, none had any experience with organ retention. They were just parents who had a mutual aim: to find out what had happened to their children and to have legislation introduced to ensure it would never happen again. The four mothers, with the support of the fathers and siblings, decided there and then to set up a support group for the many families they were sure would be affected by this practice. Fionnuala O'Reilly (RIP) was a secondary school teacher and was used to speaking, so it was decided that as the group would need a spokesperson, she was the ideal choice. Charlotte Yeates took care of all the administrative work. Margaret McKeever (RIP) and Breda Butler were involved with advising members and speaking to people on the phone constantly. They are driven, committed and relentless in their quest for truth and it is my honour to know them and be in a position to let people know the extraordinary lengths they have gone through in the past decade to get answers. I became a member in 2000.

They have often asked themselves, if they had known at the beginning what they were facing into, would they have been so quick to jump in? They all answered with a resounding and unanimous "yes". They said that they were not only fighting for justice for their own children, but were fighting for justice for all the children and adults in this country whose bodies had been plundered and who had been gutted like fish. They were fighting for all those who had been innocent victims of this national scandal.

Soon after the group formed, newspapers carried their stories and a couple of days later they were contacted by *The Late Late Show* and asked if they would appear on the following Friday. They agreed and although very nervous, Fionnuala and Charlotte headed off to the RTÉ studios in Dublin. Just as they were being fitted with microphones, the researcher came over and told them that, despite RTÉ having extended an invitation to a representative from the hospital to appear, they had refused. They were nervous enough without worrying about this.

Charlotte recalls wanting to run initially, but then Fionnuala held her hand and said, "We're not going to let them frighten us, come on." The two held hands and together walked onto the set. They spent some time discussing their cases and some of the audience were so moved they cried.

On the show, Charlotte and Fionnuala announced that they had made contact with the Minister for Health, Brian Cowen, and that they had a meeting arranged with him the following Wednesday. They also announced that they had arranged a meeting for any interested parents or families in Buswells Hotel for the following Sunday. They gave out their own home numbers on the show and by the time they got to the Green Room after the show, the RTÉ switchboard was jammed with calls from parents all around the country.

They started taking calls in the Green Room in RTÉ that night and by Monday they had received over 2,000 calls from all parts of the country. Immediately after *The Late Late Show*, there was pandemonium. They found out that all the hospitals in the country that performed post mortems were involved in this practice, and it was not just confined to children. Adults also were involved. In fact, despite the fact that the Post Mortem Inquiry was supposed to investigate from 1970 to 2000, the unauthorised removal and retention of human organs has been going on in this country since they started doing post mortems. It is the belief of Parents for Justice that any person in this State who has had a post mortem at any time, in any hospital or institution, was potentially involved in the organ retention scandal whether they know it or not. You can read more about the history of post mortems both in Ireland and abroad in Chapter 10.

They held their open meeting in Buswells the following week and were surprised that it was packed. By this time they had a legal team on board who were also present. A couple of days after *The Late Late Show*, Fionnuala O'Reilly was contacted by Breda Butler, another mother from Cork who agreed to join the committee. There were now four founding members of PFJ: Margaret, Fionnuala, Breda and Charlotte. The week after *The Late Late Show* they met with Minister Brian Cowen along with Department of Health officials in a room in a Dublin hotel.

During the meeting with the Minister, which lasted about two hours, PFJ explained to him that they wanted a public inquiry into what had happened and legislation introduced to make sure that it never again happened to any other child or adult. They explained that they had set up Parents for Justice and asked for Government funding. Mr Cowen agreed to fund the organisation and said his department would help to find out what happened to their children. He and all of his colleagues were very sympathetic. Each of the committee brought photos of their children to let them see that these were not just sets of organs but beautiful and very much loved children. PFJ set up their Helpline, which ran until 2004.

A woman who had worked as a mortician revealed that when the little ones were laid out in the mortuary chapel for prayers before they were removed for burial, she or one of the hospital staff would be present at the prayers. *This, she said, was to make sure that none of the parents or family members noticed anything unusual about their child*. In fact, she said that after the child died and a post mortem was carried out and following the removal of the children's organs, the hospital thought "they would never see the child going just in case they noticed anything and asked questions". She said that they were afraid that the parents may notice something amiss, particularly if they picked the child up. Alternatively, they might notice a leaking incision, how high up the incision came, etc. She or one of the hospital staff were present to answer any questions the parents may have had and to make sure that nobody noticed anything wrong. The mortician herself told the PFJ committee of this practice at a meeting in Limerick after she had made contact with PFJ herself.

PFJ knew that the hospital had human organs in storage and each of the other committee members asked if their child's organs were among them. Fionnuala was the only one who was told they were. She asked for them back and they agreed to give them to her. Fionnuala and her husband Bernard went to the hospital to collect the organs on 13th December 1999 – it was the fifth anniversary of their son Michael's death. When they left the hospital, they went straight to Michael's grave to bury the organs with him. Imagine the horror of having to open your child's grave and have a second burial; but imagine also the horror of *being handed your beautiful little boy's heart and lungs wrapped in cotton wool and tissue paper* – because that's what happened to Fionnuala and Bernard that day.

They were so upset, but not knowing what to expect at the hospital, they had in fact gone to their local undertaker and had asked him to make a small casket to place the organs into. When Fionnuala told PFJ what had happened in the hospital, their committee went to the Department of Health and asked them if they would make arrangements to provide caskets to any other family that was collecting organs and also to bear the cost of opening the graves, etc. The Department agreed to do this and from then on the cost of the reburials were met by the Department of Health unless the families stipulated otherwise.

Neither Breda, Margaret nor Charlotte ever got their children's organs back, and they still don't know what happened to them, ten years on.

PFJ met with Department of Health officials again before Christmas 1999. In early January 2000 there was a Cabinet re-shuffle and Brian Cowen was moved from his role to Finance and Micheál Martin became the new Minister for Health. PFJ had many, many meetings with him – as they describe it, some good, some not so good and some positively hostile. Charlotte recalls an event in 2000 that still annoys her.

"In early January another thing happened that was to shake us up and it really felt like Our Lady's Hospital were taking us for idiots. I was sitting in work looking at my daughter's post mortem report and a thought came into my head to phone the hospital and ask for the pathologist who had performed the post mortem. Remember, I had been told on 16th April 1999 when I met with the cardiologist for the first time that the pathologist who performed my daughter's post mortem was dead and that there was no one to answer any questions I might have.

"So I phoned the hospital and asked to speak to the pathologist (who was supposed to be dead). You can imagine my surprise when I was put through to the pathology lab and he came on the phone. I hid my surprise as best I could and said that he had performed my daughter's post mortem and I wanted some information about it. He took my name and my daughter's and said he was not at his desk, but he would look it up and phone me back.

"I never got the call. The next day, I phoned the hospital back and asked to speak to him, telling the girl on the end of the phone that it was an emergency and I needed to speak to him urgently; she put me right through. I'm sure she thought I was a family member. He appeared startled when he heard my name and said he had been given legal advice not to speak to me. I got very angry and threatened to go straight to the hospital to find him."

However, when Charlotte calmed down and discussed what had happened with the others it was decided to do things correctly and to ask for a formal meeting with the pathologist to find out what was going on. The meeting was arranged for the following week and the committee members arrived at the hospital to be met by the CEO, Paul Kavanagh, Consultant Pathologist, Michael McDermott, two social workers "and then," Charlotte says, "in he came – Lazarus himself". She asked him if he knew he was supposed to be dead. PFJ were then told that in fact it was the Consultant Pathologist, Dr Robert Carroll, who had died and obviously not that pathologist. However, the PFJ committee say they were all told the same thing as Charlotte and they knew what they had been told.

Apparently the meeting went from bad to worse; as one of the committee members commented, it "really was the most ridiculous situation". The pathologist was not allowed to speak to PFJ, so if one of the committee wanted to ask him a question, they had to ask either Paul Kavanagh or Michael McDermott, who in turn would ask the pathologist, who would answer them and then they in turn would relay the answer back to whoever asked the question. The meeting went on for some time and Breda asked a question about her son Joseph's organs. The pathologist answered and then, just before lunchtime, he stood up quite quickly and said he didn't feel well; he had a pain in his leg and had to leave. His colleagues helped him out of the room while the rest of the group were left there, confused to say the least. After some time, Michael McDermott came back into the room and said the pathologist was quite ill. After this, PFJ asked Dr McDermott if they could see the lab where the children's organs were kept.

As the PFJ committee recount it, "to see the look of pure panic on grown men's faces was amazing". Dr McDermott said they could not go to see where they were because there were other children's organs there and he muttered something about confidentiality. PFJ said they didn't want to see any organs, just the lab itself.

All of the committee members got up to leave the room but not before Dr McDermott made a call to clean the lab, telling someone that PFJ wanted to come down. Then he said to PFJ that they could go down in two hours, as they had to have time to "clean it up". PFJ didn't agree to this and they marched down the corridor with him, the CEO and the two social workers following close behind.

What they hadn't told him was that they knew where the organs were kept and it wasn't a lab at all. When they got close to the pathology lab, Dr McDermott ran in front of them and told them to "wait there". The "lab" was in fact two small concrete sheds attached to each other out in the back yard behind the pathology lab. The sheds were like those you might put your garden equipment in. One of the PFJ members tried the handle of the doors, but they were locked. One member of the committee took out her camera to take some pictures, but Dr McDermott jumped in front of her and asked what she thought she was doing. She told him that if he didn't want to be in the photos, then he had better move. I am told he leaned against the wall with a look of pure despair on his face.

PFJ had a meeting with the Department of Health officials immediately afterwards at three o'clock. As they were leaving the hospital, they saw an ambulance outside taking the pathologist away. When PFJ arrived at the Department and told the officials what had happened in Crumlin, they all sounded so concerned and the Chief Medical Officer, Dr Jim Kiely, went off to phone the hospital to get an update. He came back and said that the pathologist was very ill and had been taken to a hospital. The meeting in

Our Lady's Hospital continued in his absence and PFJ didn't hear anything from him in a long time.

PFJ had their first meeting with Minister Micheál Martin on 9th February 2000. During the meeting Minister Martin announced that the Government was, in fact, setting up the Inquiry PFJ asked for, but said that the actual nature of the Inquiry was yet to be decided. However, he did reassure the committee that he and his department would do everything in their power to get answers for all the families affected. The week before this meeting, PFJ had put in Dáil questions, including the following: "Had Our Lady's Hospital ever sold any of our children's organs to any pharmaceutical company or institution and had any one person benefited from them in any way?" Micheál Martin had an answer for PFJ the afternoon of their meeting. Before the meeting finished, shortly before six o'clock, he asked the committee to sit down because he had something to tell them.

He said that in reply to our question, Our Lady's had told him that they had in fact "transferred" human pituitary glands to pharmaceutical companies and these were used in the manufacture of Human Growth Medication for children with stunted growth. The Minister went on to say that if he found out that "*even one penny had changed hands, then this would put a completely different slant on things*" (see Chapter 8 "Glands for Sale"). He then went out to speak live on RTÉ's *6.01 News* from the steps of Leinster House, announcing the establishment of the Post Mortem Inquiry.

PFJ were delighted with this news and reported it back to their members. Their membership had been growing at a rapid rate, with families from all over the country making contact. They also had contact with people who now lived outside of the country in Scotland, England, New York and Canada.

Over the next few months the group had numerous meetings with the Department of Health and the Minister. Some time later, Micheál Martin informed them that a Post Mortem Inquiry was indeed being set up, but it was to be a two-tiered inquiry, the first part being in private and the second part to have full statutory powers. PFJ were dissatisfied with this and there were numerous meetings between their legal team and the Department's that sometimes ran late into the night. They also held meetings nationwide with members.

During all of this, they were still manning their helpline, 24/7. In April 2000, they had another meeting with Minister Martin. It appeared that he was trying his very best to talk the committee members into accepting the idea of a two-tier inquiry. He knew they were unhappy about this and he was right. PFJ felt the medical people would not answer questions unless they had to, and they also didn't feel that they would just turn up because the chairperson of the Inquiry asked them nicely. However, Minister Martin assured them they would; he couldn't see why a hospital would not do what the Department of Health wanted them to do. With little progress being made at the meeting, it was suggested that Minister Martin address a public PFJ meeting himself. He said yes. PFJ did not allow him to back down; they felt it was his duty to meet with and speak to members and to see for himself the complete devastation and hurt they were experiencing and to reassure them that he was really there to help. PFJ also knew that Minister Martin had lost a child himself and were hoping that he might have a better understanding of their situation.

On 3rd May 2000, Parents for Justice held a meeting for members and informed them that Department of Health officials would be in attendance and possibly the Minister himself. On the night, approximately 500 people turned up who were anxious, hurt and angry. The meeting began and the Minister, true to his word, spoke at length to members. When he said he empathised with them, it went over most people's heads. They were so angry that some shouted abuse at him and asked how he would know what it felt like to lose a child. However, to give him his due, he stood his ground and spoke about the type of Inquiry on offer and the benefits of it. It would be expeditious, cost-effective, but most of all, he had no doubt that it would get answers for all those involved in this national scandal. He also said he had no doubt that the hospitals and health boards would co-operate fully with a private inquiry. He remained afterwards for a considerable time to answer questions from the floor and to speak personally to some parents.

The committee had received some interesting information just prior to the meeting. They had learned the meeting with Our Lady's Hospital in January 2000 had been arranged by the Department of Health and Our Lady's

Hospital and that there was an official memo stating this. PFJ had every intention of announcing it at the meeting, unknown to the Minister or his officials. However, events overtook their announcement. Charlotte Yeates was sitting at the top table beside Mr Tony Morris, principal officer of the Department of Health. While the Minister was still in full flow, Tony opened his folder to check something. Out of the corner of her eye, Charlotte saw a copy of an article referring to the memo.

She describes what happened next. "I lost it completely and took the microphone and told everyone what had happened in Our Lady's Hospital. Apparently when we had asked for a meeting with the pathologist, the hospital let the Department of Health know and subsequently a memo was sent to the hospital ordering them to set up a meeting with Parents for Justice and to bring the pathologist along. He was not allowed to talk to us. It seemed very convenient to those representatives from PFJ present at the meeting that the pathologist developed a pain in his leg when he did. We were furious. How dare they treat us like that? All of our members were livid. Suffice to say that the medical legal expert who was working with us said later that 'it was the most profound use of bad language he had ever heard in his life' and he later used it with his students as an example of the effect of bad language.

"To be fair to Minister Martin, he did look totally bewildered and obviously did not know what we were talking about. He stated this and said he would investigate it. He had been made to look like a fool by his very own officials. It appeared that the Department of Health had taken us for idiots again. This was becoming a regular thing; various people in the hospitals, departments and even the Minister's office were reacting strangely. However, this just confirmed to us that, for whatever reasons, Parents for Justice was a threat to this Government. We have always felt that there is much more to the issue of unauthorised organ retention and that what we had learned was only the tip of the iceberg. Something we still believe to this very day."

Meetings continued between Parents for Justice, the Department of Health and both sets of legal people. Many months were spent in negotiations about the upcoming inquiry. In September 2000, PFJ were informed that the Government had a formula for the two-tier inquiry; the first part was to be held in private and the second part in public with full statutory powers, with the ability to compel a person to give evidence and to provide documentation. PFJ received both written and verbal confirmation from Minister Martin that if the first part of the inquiry failed for whatever reason, he would go directly into the second part. PFJ held another meeting with their members and on reading this letter of assurance from the Minister, and based on his verbal and written promises, they took a vote. It was unanimously decided that PFJ would co-operate with the Post Mortem Inquiry.

Ms Anne Dunne SC was appointed chairperson of the inquiry and her remit was to produce her report in six months. On 5th March 2001 the inquiry commenced its work in an office in Parnell Square in Dublin, after the publication of her terms of reference and her interpretation of it. She invited submissions from interested parties. Parents for Justice made a submission of behalf of the organisation and individual submissions from members as well. The committee and their legal team met with Ms Dunne at the beginning and she assured them that she would do everything in her power to get answers. However, this was not to be and Mary Harney closed down the inquiry in March 2005 shortly after becoming Minister for Health and Children.

PFJ were rather curious about some of the events surrounding the inquiry. For example, Ms Dunne began seeing some of those who had made submissions and having personal interviews with them. Those she spoke to were then asked to sign a confidentiality notice, but on legal advice, PFJ told members not to sign it.

No member of the committee was called to give evidence, with the exception of Margaret McKeever, who was suffering with cancer and wanted to give evidence while she was well enough to. The committee waited in vain to be called, but they never were, despite the fact they were the ones who knew most about this scandal.

PFJ requested an interim report from Ms Dunne, which they received in October 2002. The report showed quite obviously that Ms Dunne was having difficulties and it appeared from same that the hospitals could have been more helpful and co-operative in giving her the information she requested or the paperwork she needed. PFJ again asked Minister Martin and the Government to stop the inquiry and to place it on the statutory footing he had promised in his letter (which stated this would happen if the inquiry was not meeting its remit). However, the Minister refused, so following a mandate from members, PFJ withdrew its co-operation from the Post Mortem Inquiry in October 2002. They felt let down by the Government. They didn't have any answers and it didn't look like they would get them without a full statutory inquiry.

In light of this, PFJ members' legal people around the country urged all to issue court proceedings to keep their cases open. There is a statute of limitations and they were afraid that if the three years went by and the Post Mortem Inquiry didn't get answers in that time, they would not be able to get answers anywhere else. However, in 2008, the State Claims Agency issued letters to all those who had claims pending, pointing out that no person had had a successful case brought to court and saying that if they continued with their cases and lost (which the State Claims Agency were sure they would) then the State would come after them for costs. I have a copy of this letter and its wording is questionable.

Compensation was never an issue with Parents for Justice; I can personally vouch for this and so can the Government. The issue was answers, not money; members just wanted to know what happened to their loved ones. Three families took actions for Post Traumatic Stress Disorder and all lost their cases. Two of these families were members of PFJ and they used their own legal representation; the third family were not. There was also a test case for PFJ by their legal representation, Malcomson Law – an action against the minister for breaking his promise to provide an adequate inquiry. PFJ lost the case and the judgment essentially said that the ministerial promise was not worth the paper it was written on and that the former Minister's promise did not have to be kept by the present Minister.

The Post Mortem Inquiry trundled along like a train out of control for another couple of years. Mary Harney replaced Micheál Martin as Health Minister in September 2004 and among the very first things she did was announce that she was calling a halt to the inquiry in March 2005. PFJ appealed to her to place the inquiry on the statutory footing as promised, as it was their belief that the inquiry had failed. They still had no answers and needed the second phase to be enacted immediately. She refused. The Post Mortem Inquiry was closed down on 31st March 2005.

PFJ were informed that at 5.30 p.m. on 31st March 2005, a van arrived outside the Department of Health and fifty-four bankers' boxes were unceremoniously dumped in the foyer. They have asked numerous times for access to these boxes as they – and I – feel that the answers to many questions lie within them. Each request to view the contents has been refused.

The directors of PFJ feel that an injustice may have been done to Ms Anne Dunne. They feel that she may have discovered information that would be invaluable to the parents and families, but for whatever reasons, this is being kept secret. PFJ asked for and received an assurance that the boxes would not be destroyed or tampered with. The assurance is in writing from Minister Harney's office.

Mary Harney appointed Dr Deirdre Madden to write a report based on the information received from Ms Anne Dunne SC. The terms of reference for Madden were restricted and completely different to those issued to Dunne (to make findings from the past and recommendations for the future). Dr Madden did what she was asked – to make recommendations – but according to PFJ it was of little value to their members and did not give them the answers they so desperately wanted. Dr Madden inquired into only three Dublin hospitals, as opposed to twenty-six hospitals nationally that Dunne looked at. Her investigation was confined to children who were born alive and who died before they reached twelve years. There were many variances between the two reports, which you can read in Chapter 6. When the Madden Report was being published, PFJ asked the Department of Health for a copy of the report to be given to them twenty-four hours in advance of it being given to the media. They eventually got it less that one hour before the media and even then had to go to the Department of Health to collect it, leaving them little time to digest its contents before the media came looking for comment.

On receiving a second copy of the Executive Summary of Ms Dunne's report in March 2008, PFJ discovered other information that shocked and troubled members. They were able to establish that Ms Dunne did, in fact, make findings – they had previously been told that she did not do so. Two of the findings are particularly shocking. She found that in some cases, human organs, those belonging to beautiful little children, were left on shelves and were of no use to anyone. Essentially, this meant that children had been violated and dumped. The second finding was that when organs were taken from children, sometimes their bodies were filled with sand so that the parents would not notice any difference in the weights of their children when they held them after death. This was a very deliberate attempt to deceive parents and is totally unforgivable and certainly ethically questionable.

A Medical Certificate Stating Cause of Death is written for each person who dies. When PFJ learned of their existence, they hoped they may be able to garnish some information from them, such as the names of doctors or others who may have been able to give them information as to which organs were taken and by whom. Apparently, copies of the certificates are kept and stored by the Department of Health. *When PFJ asked for these, they were told that unfortunately there had been a flood in the Customs House, where the documents were kept, and that water had destroyed them all. Then there was a fire in the other office where some of them were kept and they were also destroyed.* The coincidences were amazing and PFJ felt that for every step forward, they went two steps back.

Charlotte explains: "We have had to resort to Freedom of Information (FOI) requests to get information. We were putting in these requests at a rapid rate and a number of years ago the Government changed the rules for applying; they introduced a charge for each FOI request. Some commentators have suggested that the introduction of a charge is to reduce the number of requests by organisations, but as far as Parents for Justice is concerned it didn't work; we kept the requests flooding in. However, we did put in a request for all the documents that all the hospitals and institutions sent in to the Post Mortem Inquiry. It took over three years and some trips to the High Court, but we got them.

"We had to appeal the hospitals' refusals to the Information Commissioner's office. In fact, Holles Street appealed the decision and took the Information Commissioner to court and made an appeal to the Supreme Court in order to stop Parents for Justice getting our hands on these documents. However, we got them.

"We were astonished. *We have brought this to the Minister Harney's attention and still this Government refuses to do anything about it.* After all, Micheál Martin did say that if money changed hands it put a different slant on things, didn't he? It is apparent that individuals did gain from the deaths of our children and loved ones. So what will this Government do? Will they continue to bury their heads in the sand?"

Over the years PFJ have also had dealings with the HSE, who are at present in the process of publishing a report about the number of organs still retained in Irish hospitals. They have had internal audits in the hospitals and appointed Ms Michaela Willis from the UK, herself a bereaved mother and previous Chairperson of NACOR (UK organ retention support group) who is currently working in the Bereavement Partnership in the UK. PFJ have been in contact with her since 1999. She has been employed to carry out an independent review of this audit here, which she has now been doing since June 2007. The latest date for the publication of this report was January 2009; at the time of going to press there is still no sign of it.

Over the last decade, I have learned much from PFJ and they in turn have made it their business to know what they are talking about. Their belief that this Government is trying to keep its head down over the issue of organ retention has been confirmed time and time again. However, as Charlotte points out, "surely this Government has learned that PFJ and its members are not going away and we will continue to ask the questions we have been asking now for ten years. We just want to find out what happened to our children and loved ones; is that such a terrible thing? We have come across many obstacles since the scandal of organ retention became public knowledge. During that time we have lost two of our founder members to cancer – Margaret McKeever and Fionnuala O'Reilly, both young women and both determined to find these answers. We made promises to both that we would continue with our mission and we intend to keep that promise."

PFJ, and indeed I myself, are determined to overcome whatever obstacles are placed in our way to continue to fight for justice, for truth and for answers, for all the children and adults in this country who are victims of this national scandal. The HSE withdrew funding from PFJ in December 2007 and they had to vacate their offices. However, now they just do the same work except they do it from their homes.

For the past decade, getting information has been a long and arduous process, with obstacles placed at every juncture and every request contested, denied or ignored. What information that is available has been battled hard for. What information hasn't been made available will be battled for even harder. *The Government may be winning a battle, but Parents for Justice, along with myself, fully intend to win the war.*

I feel it appropriate that the final words of this chapter come from Charlotte Yeates, spokesperson of PFJ. "We will always be here asking the same questions that we asked on the very first day we met Brian Cowen in December 1999. It's ironic that now that he is Taoiseach of the country he won't meet with us. *May God forgive him, former Health Ministers and the Government, for they have let down tens of thousands of people in this country. Shame on all of them.*"

CHAPTER 5

Ron's Story:
Our Precious Angel

"To a father, when his child dies, the future dies; to a child, when his parents die, the past dies."

BERTHOLD AUERBACH

Elizabeth McCarten was a little girl who loved life, lived it to the full and won medals for swimming and dancing. She loved pop groups Boney M and Bucks Fizz and had a natural flair for sporting activities, with rugby being a firm favourite. She also loved ballet and horse-riding, in which she partook on a regular basis. She excelled at school and loved playing practical jokes on people. As a small child, Elizabeth loved Beatrix Potter and would know if her father ever tried to skip a page at bedtime – as most parents do! She was a very friendly girl who was just fourteen when she died and her last word was "Mummy".

Elizabeth was the only daughter of Ron and Edna McCarten, originally from the Lake District in the UK but living in Ireland since 1972. Like most little girls, Elizabeth was the apple of her parents' eye and got on well with her two brothers. Her father Ron spoke to me in the hope that it will help contribute to finding out the truth; getting a proper apology; and getting funding reinstated for PFJ. Ron tells us Elizabeth's story . . .

Elizabeth was born in January 1971 in Oldham, UK. She was of low birth weight (four pounds) so she was taken to the Special Care Unit, where we spent most of our time. Everyone remarked how beautiful she was. My wife Edna was sent home, but Elizabeth remained in hospital. We spent a lot of time with her, but every time Edna asked to feed her she had either just been fed, or wasn't due for a feed and so remained in the incubator. After a couple of weeks I asked when they thought we could take her home and I was told "tomorrow". I was a little worried because she was still so small and asked the nurse if she thought Elizabeth would be okay, but the nurse said it wasn't for her to say and I should speak to a doctor.

Before we set off for the hospital the following morning, I phoned the sister to arrange to see a doctor when we got there. My parents were at the hospital when we arrived and we sat on the side of a bed. The doctor and a nurse carrying Elizabeth came in. The doctor asked us what the problem was. I could see that Elizabeth had a small trace of blood on her head. I asked him what it was. He replied that it was probably a remainder of afterbirth and proceeded to wipe it off with his finger. I thought this was rather strange, given that it was three weeks since her birth.

My wife Edna, a nurse, immediately asked if she had Down Syndrome. We were told that she did and, as is common with Down Syndrome babies, she also had serious heart problems. We took her home and shortly afterwards in February she developed pneumonia. We nursed her ourselves, but she didn't appear to be getting any better, so we brought her back to the hospital. The same doctor who tried to fob us off the day we took her home happened to be on duty, so he examined Elizabeth. He told us she was dying and that if she didn't die now she would die next winter. Edna was furious and said she never wanted Elizabeth to be treated by that doctor again; as a result, she never saw him again.

In September I came over to Ireland, while Edna stayed in the UK. She was worried that, at eleven months, Elizabeth weighed only eleven pounds. I continued to go back and forth between Ireland and the UK from September until January when I got the house and we all came to Ireland. Elizabeth and Edna stayed with friends in Arklow while the house was being done up. However, Elizabeth became ill and we took her to Our Lady's Hospital for Sick Children in Crumlin, where she was seen by the consultant who she went to for the duration of her life.

Elizabeth thrived against the odds and enjoyed Montessori and primary school. At twelve she began to slow down a little and was diagnosed with a thyroid deficiency and put on the drug thyroxine. We were due to go to the UK for a visit and the consultant gave us his telephone number and said to ring him day or night if we had any problems. From January to June, Elizabeth was very poorly and was in Our Lady's. She picked up an infectious disease and was sent to the hospital in Ballyfermot for infectious diseases.

We took her home from there and she resumed her ballet dancing and horse-riding, among other things. Unlike many children with Down Syndrome, Elizabeth had the most delicate hands with long fingers. I would often marvel at how pretty they were.

In 1984, when Elizabeth was fourteen, we entered into discussions with doctors about the possibility of heart surgery. We were told that the improvement to her quality of life would be substantial and that it was worth considering. Edna and I went home and discussed it at length and in June we telephoned our professor and said we wanted to go ahead with it. The wheels were put in motion and in July Elizabeth underwent surgery. It appeared to be successful and she was thriving. She was sharing a room with another girl who had undergone the same operation, so she had a companion. Edna and the mother of the other child were called outside the room, where it was explained to them that there was a slight risk of kidney failure.

Sadly, Elizabeth's kidneys failed, but the other child was fine. When I was visiting Elizabeth, I noticed that her scar was very inflamed and red. I went home later that night while Edna stayed. Edna popped to the loo and when she got back to the room Elizabeth turned to her and simply said "Mummy" and passed away. I got a call at home to say Elizabeth had taken a turn for the worse. I rushed to the hospital, with so many things going through my head. When I got there I tried hard to contain my emotions, but my darling daughter was gone.

I was asked if I would consent to an autopsy and I gave my permission in the hope it might help others. There were no forms, just a verbal agreement.

Her funeral was a celebration of her life and as the hearse pulled out, a host of swallows flew over it. I like to think Elizabeth had something to do with that.

As soon as the scandal broke, I called the hospital and we were given an appointment. I just knew in my heart that Elizabeth had been affected long before it was confirmed at the meeting that her organs "had not been returned". When we asked what had happened to them, we were told that they had been incinerated. We were completely devastated. When we joined Parents for Justice, we were torn apart at having to relive everything over again; it was so painful. We just wanted the truth and an apology, but have got nowhere in the past eight years.

In January 2008, we wrote to Minister for Health, Mary Harney TD, asking for funding to be made available to PFJ so they could operate properly again. We received a standard reply from her private secretary saying the matter was receiving attention. At the time of giving this interview in late 2008 we still await a response to our letter of January 2008.

My beautiful, funny, lively, intelligent and witty daughter deserves the truth, and so do we. People need to know what the organ retention scandal was really all about and we need to know why it has been clouded in secrecy. *Tell us the truth.*

CHAPTER 6

A Tale of Two Reports

"The truth is that our finest moments are most likely to occur when we are feeling deeply uncomfortable, unhappy or unfulfilled. For it is only in such moments, propelled by our discomfort, that we are likely to step out of our ruts and start searching for different ways or truer answers."

M SCOTT PECK

Much of the organ retention scandal has centred around two specific reports: the Dunne Report and the Madden Inquiry. One made history, while the other reported upon it. One was made public, while the other is kept secret under lock and key. One cost in the region of €20 million and took four years to compile, while the other cost €400,000 and was produced in six months. Both have been the subject of great debate and speculation. However, if you were to hazard a guess at which has been made public and which has not, you would naturally assume that the report, which cost €20 million, was the one that was made public. Unbelievably, you would be wrong.

The fifty-four boxes of information gathered by Anne Dunne SC were never made public. They lie in a Dublin warehouse; their contents a mystery. Ethics expert Dr Deirdre Madden, who was commissioned by the Department of Health and Children to produce a report based on the findings of the Dunne Inquiry, then produced the Madden Report. However, this is where it gets a little complicated. As outlined elsewhere in this book, the initial Dunne Inquiry (a non-statutory inquiry), was conducted in private, took four years and was wound up, unfinished, without ever producing a report or any findings – or so we were led to believe. Minister for Health Mary Harney was accused in the media at the time of hiding behind the then Attorney-General, Ruairi Brady, who decided that, in the interests of "natural justice", these 3,500 pages could not be publicly released. This debacle was then further compounded – at yet more expense (€400,000 to be precise) – when Dr Madden was appointed by the Department of Health and Children to produce a report based on the findings of the defunct Dunne Inquiry. The ensuing Madden Report was released to the Minister in December 2005 and to the public in 2006 and presented the facts relating to post mortem practice in Ireland (including organ retention). It made fifty recommendations; of course, and as we all know only too well, a recommendation may or may not be acted upon.

Time Limits and Hospitals Included in the Dunne and Madden Inquiries

Before the Post Mortem Inquiry was established, it was reasonably assumed that *any* hospital in the State that had ever carried out a post mortem would be included and subsequently investigated. However, this proved not to be the case and it took many meetings with the Minister for Health, Micheál Martin, his officials and the legal teams from his Department and Parents for Justice to agree to confine the investigation to a thirty-year period from 1970 until 2000 and to include just twenty-six hospitals. The reason for the latter limitation was cited as being that if every single hospital in the State were to be included, then the terms of reference would be far too wide.

The time scale 1970–2000 was decided to contain the date to a workable timeframe. However, there was a general acceptance and acknowledgement by all parties at the meeting that the unauthorised removal and retention of human organs had always been part of the post mortem procedure in Ireland. It would be ludicrous to suggest that on 1st January 1970, unauthorised organ retention suddenly began, and just as suddenly stopped on 31st December 1999. There are some known cases that go back to the 1960s. There had to be some concession made for those who wanted to query a post mortem outside the imposed dates set by the inquiry, so Minister Martin agreed any such queries would also be included in the inquiry process.

Terms of Reference
The following are the terms of reference from both reports and an explanation as to the differences between them. Replication of some of the facts is unavoidable, but perhaps affords the opportunity to hammer home the enormity of the scandal we are dealing with.

The Post Mortem Inquiry

(as Chaired by Ms Anne Dunne SC) Terms of Reference:

To review all post mortem examination practices, policies and procedures in the State since 1970, and in particular as it relates to organ removal, retention, storage and disposal and by reference to prevailing standards both inside and outside the State. To examine the application of these practices, policies and procedures in hospitals generally, and in particular their application in the hospitals listed in the Appendix. The Inquiry will address the hospitals' policies, practices and procedures in this area of organ removal, retention, storage and disposal, the necessity for such practices and the manner in which they were carried out. The Inquiry will take account of best practice regarding post mortem examination in and outside of the State together with the reasonable expectations of parents of deceased children and next of kin in such circumstances. In particular, the Inquiry will:

1 *Examine the hospitals' policies and practices relating to obtaining consent from parents and next of kin for post mortem examinations, organ removal, retention, storage and disposal.*

2 *Examine the hospitals' procedures and practices relating to retained organs, including the reasons for such retention, the hospitals' management of such retention and storage of organs (including record keeping) and to any other arrangements*

relating to such organs and the practices adopted for ultimately dealing with retained organs, including those with pharmaceutical companies in relation to those retained organs.

3 *Review the nature and appropriateness of the hospitals' overall response to parents of children and next of kin of persons on whom a post mortem examination was performed.*

4 *Examine any specific cases in any hospital as it deems appropriate in relation to post mortem examinations and any post mortem examination related matters.*

However it will be at the discretion of the Inquiry to examine any other relevant matters, which arise in the course of the Inquiry into post mortem policies, practices and procedures in the State since 1970. In these Terms of Reference post mortem examination refers to any post mortem examination, including, where appropriate, any post mortems directed by the Coroner.

The Inquiry will make its final report, including its findings, to the Minister for Health and Children within six months, unless otherwise determined by the Minister. It will make recommendations to the Minister on any changes it considers necessary on foot of its findings.

The Report will include confirmation that the Inquiry received all the information and co-operation from health agencies, persons employed therein and any other persons, which it considers necessary to form its opinions and arrive at its conclusions. In the event of deficiencies arising in these areas, which the Inquiry considers materially limited the scope of its investigations, the Report will identify same.

In her interpretation of the Terms of Reference, Ms Dunne stated the following:

The term "Hospitals" means all hospitals in the State in which post mortems were carried out and/or hospitals, which requested, directed or authorised post mortems to be carried out at another location, since 1970, and in particular, but not exclusively, the hospitals listed in the Appendix.

This Appendix contained a list of twenty-six hospitals around Ireland When the government restricted the inquiry, Ms Dunne was told to concentrate on only three of the hospitals. It was the report on these three hospitals – Our Lady's, Temple Street and Holles Street – to which Dr Madden confined her investigations.

The Madden Report
(as Chaired by Dr Deirdre Madden) Terms of Reference:

1 *To enquire into Policies and Practices relating to the removal, retention and disposal of organs from children who have undergone post mortem examinations in the State since 1970.*

2 *To enquire into allegations that pituitary glands were removed from children undergoing post-mortem examination for sale to pharmaceutical companies within and outside the State.*

3 *To examine professional practice in relation to the information given to parents in respect of the removal, retention and disposal of tissue or organs and the appropriateness of obtaining consent.*

4 *To review the manner in which hospitals responded to concerns raised by bereaved families relating to post mortem practices carried out on children.*

5 *To make recommendations for any legislative and/or policy change as deemed appropriate.*

Note: Organs removed with consent for transplantation purposes are excluded from the Inquiry.

Notable Differences between the Two Reports

Parents for Justice studied the reports closely and in so doing noted some glaring variances:

1 DUNNE was asked to investigate twenty-six hospitals in the State and was in the process of doing so when she was told to concentrate on just three Dublin hospitals. A lot of the information contained in the fifty-four bankers' boxes given to Minister Harney contains information relating to these other hospitals.

MADDEN was asked to investigate the same three hospitals in Dublin based on the information in the fifty-four boxes.

2 DUNNE investigation included all persons who had post mortems – adults and children.

MADDEN investigation concentrated only on children who were born alive and who died before the age of twelve years, excluding thousands of people and also about fifty per cent of PFJ membership.

3 DUNNE was asked to make findings from the past. In other words, she was required to find out exactly what happened to our children and loved ones and to inform the parents/families. She was also asked to make recommendations for the future.

MADDEN was asked to make recommendations for the future only, not findings about what happened in the past.

4 DUNNE interviewed witnesses, parents and families.

MADDEN did not.

Recommendations of the Madden Report
26th January 2006

Although the Madden Report did not give answers to the questions most parents have, it did make fifty recommendations to the Government for change, and these are listed below. One can only hope they are acted upon because thus far few of them have been.

1   *Need for Legislation*

1.1 Legislation must be introduced as a matter of urgency to ensure that no post mortem examination will be carried out on the body of a deceased child and no organ will be retained from a post mortem examination for any purpose whatsoever without the authorisation of the child's parents/guardian, or the authorisation of the Coroner in the appropriate case.

1.2 The removal of organs from the body of a deceased child at post mortem is carried out as a necessary part of the examination of the body and diagnosis of the cause of death. It must be made clear in legislation that a post mortem examination includes the necessary removal of organs for this purpose. Subject to Recommendation 2.3, parents must be clearly informed of this prior to their authorisation of the Hospital post mortem examination.

1.3 The retention of organs at post mortem may be necessary in certain circumstances in order to make an accurate diagnosis of the detailed cause of death. Subject to Recommendation 2.3, parents should be clearly informed of this prior to their authorisation of the Hospital post mortem examination. As part of this process parents must be informed as to the reasons for the retention, the likely retention period, and must be offered such further information as they require.

1.4 Subject to Recommendation 2.3, parents must be informed of the benefit of retained organs for audit, education and research, and given the opportunity to authorise retention for such purposes. Parents must also be given choices in relation to subsequent return, burial or cremation of the organs.

1.5 It is recommended that legislation should provide that where both parents are legal guardians of a deceased child either parent should be able to give authorisation for a Hospital post mortem examination, though ideally both should participate in the decision. Situations may exceptionally arise in which the parents of the child disagree as to whether or not to authorise a Hospital post mortem on their child. In such situations or where only one parent is the legal guardian, the hospital would be legally entitled to proceed with the post mortem with the authorisation of one parent. However, best practice would ordinarily be not to proceed with a hospital post mortem in the face of objection of either parent irrespective of their marital or living arrangements.

1.6 The health and safety aspects of the storage, use and disposal of human organs derived from post mortem examinations must be regulated by Legislation.

1.7 Legislation must prohibit the removal of human organs from a deceased child at post mortem examination for supply by hospitals to any pharmaceutical company or other third party without the knowledge or authorisation of the parents. Where such organs are supplied, such arrangements must be clearly approved by the hospital management and documented, and all information supplied to the parents on request.

1.8 An appropriate legislative framework must be put in place to govern Hospital post mortems. A regulatory model that facilitates guidelines to be updated when necessary to keep pace with medical and scientific developments is recommended. Legislation must clearly set out the purposes for which a post mortem examination may be performed. In order to restore and maintain public confidence in the system, the legislation must set out clear safeguards for patients and their families, and encourage medical education and research. Penalties must be imposed for non-compliance of these safeguards.

1.9 Although not specifically addressed within the Terms of Reference of this Report, it is clear that Human Tissue Legislation is urgently required to deal with issues relating to removal, storage and uses of human biological material from the living and the deceased. Provision should be made in such legislation to facilitate and encourage medical education and training, and approved medical research, while maintaining the principle of respect for the donor, the deceased person and the bereaved.

2 Information for Parents and the Authorisation Process

2.1 The grief and anguish suffered by parents who discovered that their children's organs had been retained and in some cases later disposed of by hospitals, was caused by a failure by medical professionals to communicate openly and honestly with parents at the time of death. The main aim of this Report is to place parents/guardians at the centre of decision-making and control in respect of Hospital post mortem examinations to be carried out on their children. However, the doctrine and language of informed consent is considered to be inappropriate in this context and is not recommended.

2.2 It is recommended that the alternative concept of authorisation be adopted. This is a stronger and more powerful recognition of the active role and choice of parents' decision making in relation to post mortems. It is recommended that systems and policies be put in place to ensure that all parents are offered such information as they require to make the decision as to whether or not to authorise a post mortem to be performed on their child. This must be viewed as a process and not a once-off event.

2.3 Parents must be given the option of authorising a post mortem examination to be carried out on their child on the understanding that this is being performed to provide further information as to the cause of death and the possible effects of treatment. Some parents may wish to authorise a post mortem without wanting to receive any further information or consultation. Their right not to receive this information must be respected. It must be made clear to them that they can come back with a future request for information *at any time*. For those parents who choose this option, it must be stated on the authorisation forms that this includes authorisation of all actions necessary as part of that examination. The accompanying information booklet to be given to parents to read if they so choose must explain that this will include removal and sampling of organs, and may include retention of organs for diagnostic purposes. It must be made clear that organs retained at post mortem examinations will not be used for any purpose other than diagnosis without the authorisation of the parents/guardian.

2.4 If they require further information prior to authorisation, parents must be told that the performance of a post mortem examination involves the examination of the body of the deceased child. It includes the dissection of the body and the removal of organs, tissue samples and blood/bodily fluids. It is carried out to provide information about or confirm the cause of death, to investigate the effect and efficacy of a medical or surgical intervention, to obtain information regarding the health of another person/future person, and for audit, education, training or research purposes. Parents must be made aware that in certain circumstances it may be necessary to retain organs in order to complete the examination.

2.5 Parents should also be informed of the potential benefits of retention in terms of education, training and research. If the retention period is short, it must be made clear to the parents that it may be possible to delay the funeral in order that the organs may be reunited with the body. In other cases, they must be made aware of their options in relation to disposal of the organs at a later date.

2.6 Parents must be given the option of authorising a limited post mortem. They may choose to limit the examination to certain organs, but in making that choice, must be informed that this will mean that samples will be taken from the organs being examined, and information will not be available on other organs, which may have contributed to the child's death.

2.7 It is recommended that the means by which and the place in which parents are informed about the post mortem process be as sensitive and respectful as possible in the circumstance. If possible, a dedicated bereavement room should be available and adequate time should be given to parents to consider the issue.

Information must be offered to parents/ guardians and an open dialogue entered into *prior* to the authorisation of a Hospital post mortem. The information must be presented in a clear and comprehensive but sensitive manner. A bereavement liaison officer should assist the parents in getting the information they need prior to their decision.

2.8 It is not intended to make specific recommendations as to the most appropriate person to discuss post mortems with the family, as this is deemed unnecessarily prescriptive. It will usually be a senior clinician who has a relationship with the parents, though a team approach may be preferable in some cases, involving nursing and midwifery staff in particular. Where possible, consultation with the hospital pathologist should take place prior to discussion with the parents so as to concentrate that discussion on issues of most relevance to the particular child. If the parents so request it, a pathologist must be available to answer specific queries or explain the post mortem in more detail.

2.9 The confidentiality of the post mortem report raises issues regarding its disclosure to other persons. Hospital post mortem reports must be made available to the consultant clinician who treated the child, if there was one, and the child's general practitioner. It is recommended that the post mortem report must also be offered to parents of deceased children with advice to seek any necessary explanations from their General Practitioner, consultants or the relevant pathologists. Where possible, a follow-up meeting between parents and clinicians must be arranged to discuss the post mortem findings in as much detail as the parents require. If necessary or desirable in the circumstances, the pathologist may also be requested to attend such meetings. This facility must be made known to parents at the time of the authorisation of the Hospital post mortem examination. Protocols must be put in place to provide a structure whereby parents receive a timely and appropriate response to their request for information.

2.10 Standardised authorisation forms and clearly written information booklets must be drafted and used on a national basis to ensure consistency and transparency.

3   *Coroners' Post Mortems*

3.1 The recommendations of the Report of the Working Group on the Coroners Service must be implemented without further delay. A new Coroners Act must be enacted to clarify the legal duties and rights of Coroners, and the procedures to be followed from the reporting of a death through to holding of inquests. Clear structures must be established to deal with information to be provided to families, the appointment of a Coroners' officer to liaise with parents following a post mortem, and the provision of support to families through the inquest process.

3.2 The role and responsibility of the Coroners' office in relation to communicating with families must be clearly outlined in Coroners' rules. Although it is common for the Coroners' post mortem to take place within a hospital, hospital staff are obliged not to discuss the post mortem with the family as this is a matter for the Coroner. This can create difficulty and tension between the hospital and the family and must be avoided by clear mechanisms being put in place to inform families of the process and their rights. Disclosure arrangements with relatives must be reviewed so as to ensure that relatives are kept informed as far as possible, subject to the proviso that there may be circumstances in which the Coroner cannot provide full information because of the nature of his inquiry and any accompanying criminal investigation. Coroners' post mortem reports must state when organs have been retained and the reason for retention.

3.3 Where a Coroners' post mortem is required, parents must be so informed clearly and without delay. They must be told that their consent is not required. An information booklet setting out the powers and functions of the Coroner, and the procedural aspects of the coronial jurisdiction, may be made available to the family. They must also be told that organs may only be retained as part of this process for as long as is necessary to establish the cause of death and other relevant matters relating to the child's death. Parents must be told that they have the opportunity to decide on the disposal of the organs once the Coroner's purposes have been satisfied. Good effective communication in all aspects of this discussion is of paramount importance.

3.4 Coroners are entitled and obliged at law to direct retention of organs to assist in the investigation of the cause of death. Retention for any other purpose such as teaching or research is outside the remit of the Coroner and, if it is to take place, must be clearly authorised by the child's parent/guardian.

3.5 The legal position pertaining to the status of organs lawfully retained as part of a Coroner's post mortem examination must be clarified by legislation. Pathologists performing post mortem examinations at the request of the

Coroner must have clear protocols agreed with the Coroner for the retention of organs.

3.6 In some cases there may be cultural or religious objections by the family of the deceased to the holding of a post mortem examination and/or the retention of organs. Insofar as it is possible to do so, these objections should be respected. However, such objections cannot interfere with the lawful exercise of the Coroners' jurisdiction and obligation to investigate the cause of death.

3.7 All instructions from the Coroner to the pathologist must be documented in writing. The responsibilities and rights of pathologists carrying out Coroners' post mortems must be clearly established by legislation.

3.8 It is recommended that the new Coroners Act provide for options to be made to families of deceased persons in relation to disposition of the organs when the death investigation has been concluded. These options should include return of the organs for burial, donation of the organs to an appropriate hospital for teaching or research, burial in a hospital plot, or cremation. The cost implications of these options should also be dealt with by the legislation.

3.9 In the case of a Coroner's post mortem, parents must be given the post mortem report on request, though the timing of its release may depend on whether or not an inquest is required in the circumstances. This must be made clear to parents in information provided to them from the outset of the process.

4. *Hospital Post Mortem Policy*

4.1 All post mortem examinations must be carried out by a qualified pathologist in accordance with the professional guidelines of relevant training bodies. This does not necessarily mean that a specialised paediatric pathologist will perform all paediatric post mortems as this may be impossible from a resource and personnel perspective.

4.2 Standardised authorisation forms must be drafted in consultation with interested parties and used in all hospitals in conjunction with standard information booklets. A copy of the authorisation form must be kept in the patient's medical record as well as sent to the pathology department where the post mortem is carried out. The pathologist must ensure that authorisation has been given prior to proceeding with the examination. *Parents must also be given a copy of the authorisation form.*

4.3 Measures must be adopted by all health service providers to ensure that all patient care staff receive mandatory training in responding to grief and bereavement.

4.4 Each hospital must have a bereavement liaison officer available to offer practical help and support to bereaved families and staff caring for those families. This officer must liaise with the relevant pathology department and should have a good understanding of pathology practices so as to provide assistance to the family if required. Although it is the clinician's responsibility to discuss the post mortem with the parent, this may be done as part of a team approach with the bereavement liaison officer, who may provide appropriate follow-up support.

4.5 Post mortems must be viewed as a continuation of patient care and therefore part of clinical governance within the hospital. Although professional autonomy dictates the technical detail of the performance of the post mortem, responsibility for the administrative aspects of the process rests with hospital management who must make certain that protocols are in place to ensure all legal requirements as to authorisation and record keeping are satisfactorily complied with. This also requires that an effective audit of post mortem practices be regularly undertaken to reassure the public that past practices cannot recur and that the hospitals' policies and practices conform to current legal requirements.

4.6 Health care providers must ensure that health services employees are instructed in post mortem policy and relevant procedures for giving information to parents. This must be included as part of the induction for new entrants to the health care service.

4.7 An independent audit must be carried out of currently retained organs in all hospitals in the State. The Department of Health and Children and the Health Service Executive should engage in a public information campaign informing relatives that they may reclaim any currently retained organs within a 12-month period from the date of this Report (2005). This should be organised and managed via a central enquiry line rather than by individual hospitals. Families who do not contact hospitals in this regard should not be approached with this information. Their right not to know must be respected, provided reasonable efforts have been made to disseminate information publicly.

4.8 If, after this 12-month period, organs remain unclaimed, they must be disposed of respectfully by the hospital in line with written policies.

This must be done in accordance with health and safety regulations and will entail either burial in a hospital plot, or cremation. Conformity with national policies and regulations must be demonstrated in accurate record keeping and monitored by periodic audit.

4.9 Accurate and detailed record keeping of retention and disposal of organs at post mortem must be maintained in all pathology departments in accordance with best practice guidelines. Physical disposal or return of organs to families must be carried out by technical services staff or the bereavement liaison officer respectively, in accordance with hospital policy and the wishes of the parent/guardian.

4.10 It is recommended that guidance be given by the hospital to families regarding burial or cremation of the organs and that they be advised to use an undertaker for this process. An information sheet setting out the necessary information must be given to families to whom organs are being returned.[1]

4.11 Where organs are to be disposed of by the hospital in accordance with the wishes of the family, this must be done in accordance with

[1] *Author's note:* I didn't receive one in November 2008.

126

health and safety guidelines established by the Department of Health and Children. These guidelines must ensure that the organs are treated with dignity and respect insofar as this can be facilitated by the safe and hygienic disposal method chosen.

4.12 Clear national protocols must be put in place by the Department of Health and Children and the Health Service Executive to deal with queries from families in respect of post mortem practices as well as the provision of standardised forms to be used on a national basis. The language to be used in such forms must be clear and comprehensible and must avoid medical or legal terminology as much as possible. Existing guidelines as produced by the National Working Group on Organ Retention in 2002, and adopted by the National Chief Officers in 2003 may be used as the basis on which to make any adaptations recommended in this Report. This should be done in consultation with relevant stakeholders.

5   *Public Awareness*

5.1 Measures should be taken to inform the public that post mortem examinations are carried out to safeguard health and well-being. The welfare and best interest of the families of the deceased, as well as that of society in general, requires steps to be taken to promote the importance of the autopsy in our health care system.

5.2   The public should be made aware of the process of a post mortem examination, the fact that organs are removed for examination and small specimens kept as part of their medical records for further tests, in their interests. They should also be made aware that in certain circumstances, it may be necessary to retain whole organs for examination and that the body may not always be returned intact for burial.

5.3   The Department of Health and Children should engage in a public education and information programme to ensure that members of the public are informed as much as possible as to the post mortem procedure, the value of retention of organs and tissue, the importance of pathology practices in our healthcare system, the value of post mortems in the education of medical professionals and in the carrying out of significant research, and the rights of families in this regard. Restoration of public confidence in medical practice, and specifically pathology practices, is vitally important to encourage a higher rate of post mortems in our hospitals.

6   *Medical Education and Training*

6.1 It is recommended that medical and nursing students be permitted and encouraged to attend post mortem examinations. Legislation should provide for such educational viewing to be sought from the parent/guardian of the deceased child or the Coroner as appropriate. Guidelines should be drawn up to ensure that such attendance would be carried out in a controlled and respectful manner.

6.2 As part of the education and training of medical professionals, increased attention must be paid to communication skills and the legal and ethical issues involved in the removal and use of human organs and tissue. All relevant hospital staff must be trained in relation to the authorisation process.

6.3 It is recommended that anonymised organs currently retained in pathology museums for teaching purposes should be maintained as a valuable educational resource. Any proposed inclusion of an organ in such a museum in the future must be authorised and documented.

7   *Medical Research*

7.1 In any discussion about organ retention, parents must be given information about potential uses and benefits of retention for purposes of education and research, unless they indicate that they do not wish to receive such information. Sometimes comfort may be afforded to parents who feel that something positive may come from their child's death. It is recommended that organs may be removed and retained from the body of a deceased child at a Hospital post mortem for purposes of education and research, only where the removal and retention for such purpose has been authorised by the child's parent/guardian.

7.2 It is recommended that authorisation of retention for research purposes may be general or specific. Choice must be given to parents as to what form of authorisation they wish to give. A general authorisation will facilitate the use of the retained organs for research purposes that are not presently foreseeable. A specific authorisation may limit the research use of the organs by prohibiting certain types of research being carried out with the organs. The authorisation form must enable full account to be taken of parents' views in this regard.

7.3 Where the purpose of the organ retention following a post mortem examination is research, it is recommended that in addition to the requirement that the retention be authorised, the research must be also subject to ethical review by an approved Research Ethics Committee.

7.4   Parents may not wish to be told the details of a post mortem examination and may nonetheless choose to authorise such examination to take place. In these circumstances, authorisation of organ removal and retention for any purposes other than diagnosis of the cause of death cannot be presumed and must therefore be specifically obtained for education, training and research.

Glands for Grabs

It is worth mentioning here, although I have devoted an entire chapter to it, that the report clearly states that money was exchanged for pituitary glands. For example: "In 1978 the payment was IR£1.50 per pituitary gland collected. In about November 1981 the payment was increased to IR£2.50, and by 1985 the payment had risen to between IR£3.00 and IR£3.50 for each pituitary gland delivered." These are small amounts, I agree, but when you start multiplying them by thousands, this quickly changes the perspective.

It is also known from the Madden Report which hospitals supplied glands (see Chapter 8). What is not known, however, is whether the glands were from adults or children. However, does it really matter which they came from? Both were denied the basic right of dignity and respect in death. It is also a clear indication of how widespread the scandal was.

Aftermath of the Madden Report

Sadly it appears that words like "immediate", "speedy" and "without delay" do not apply when it comes to change in our system. Despite the Madden Report making a number of *"urgent"* recommendations in 2005, the majority *still* have to be acted upon. In an effort to establish what was going on and when we could expect to see action, I contacted the Press Office for the Department of Health and Children. I liaised with the same woman throughout my research for this book where it concerned the Department of Health and she was most helpful. Sadly, Minister Harney was not, when she could have shed so much light on this and answered so many questions.

I decided to keep my questions short and to the point, focusing only on the Madden Report and its recommendations and the lack of implementation thus far.

Q. One of the recommendations of the Madden Report, 2005, was that an independent audit was to be carried out of currently retained organs in all hospitals in the State. Was this audit ever carried out and if so, what was the total number of organs still being retained?

A. *The HSE commissioned an independent audit of retained organs by Ms Michaela Willis, who is a member of the UK Human Tissue Authority and founder and Chief Executive of the National Bereavement Partnership. Ms Willis was also the founder and chair of the UK's National*

*Committee relating to Organ Retention, Chair
of the Bristol Heart Children's Action Group,
and Non-Executive Director of the Retained
Organs Commission for a three-year term. Ms
Willis is expected to present her report to the
HSE in the near future.*

[Note: I already knew most of this information. In fact, I
appeared to know even more than the Department seems
to know or neglected to mention. Ms Willis is herself a
bereaved parent – her son died after surgery. Not
mentioning this seemed a rather glaring omission given
the context of my questions. I decided to plod on with my
questioning.]

Q. The Report recommended that the DoHC and
the HSE should engage in a public information
campaign. When and how was this campaign
carried out?

A. *The public information campaign will be
undertaken by HSE once Ms Willis's report is
received and examined.*

[Again this was to be undertaken in 2005. By now I was
getting impatient. Dr Madden had made this recommendation in 2005 and I clearly recalled something about a
twelve-month timeframe from the date of the report. I
checked the report again, and there, in section 4.7, was
exactly what I was looking for (see above). This line of
questioning was proving fruitless, but I persevered.]

Q. What changes in policy and practice has the Department overseen when the need for a post mortem arises?

A. *The most significant change was on foot of a Directive issued on 9th December 1999 by the Chief Medical Officer of the Department, at the request of the Minister for Health and Children, Mr Brian Cowen TD* [and now Taoiseach], *to the Chief Executive Officers of all health boards and hospitals, that a policy of informed consent by next of kin should operate in respect of post-mortem examination and organ retention. The Chief Executive Officers were also asked in a letter of 17th December 1999 to adopt a systematic and comprehensive response to the concerns of parents and families affected by organ retention. This response was to ensure that the individual needs of parents and families would be met and should, at a minimum, include the provision of specific information, counselling and other appropriate support services where required. The response also included a provision for financial support in individual cases to families who wished to make private arrangements for interment of retained organs.*

[Funding was taken away from PFJ and counselling for bereaved parents in 2008, though. It appears what is given with one hand is taken away with another. The response continued on, but I had the information I needed. The man, who as Minister for Health and who had enacted this Directive, became silent as Taoiseach. It didn't make any sense to me. In fact, it still doesn't . . . Lord, what a tangled web this scandal is.]

Q. Did the Department oversee the recommendation that a Bereavement Liaison Officer was available in all hospitals?

A. *The appointment of Bereavement Liaison Officers in hospitals is a matter for the Health Service Executive (HSE), overseen by the Department of Health and Children.*

Q. At exactly what stage is development of legislation to introduce a human tissue act?

A. *On 23rd September 2008, the Government approved the preparation of the General Scheme and Heads of a Human Tissue Bill to regulate the removal, retention, storage, use and disposal of human tissue from deceased persons and consent for the use of donated tissue from living persons for the purpose of transplantation and research.*

[The timeframe from preparation to enactment is anybody's guess.]

Brian's Story:
Our Pride and Joy

"The death of my daughter is a subject I talk about briefly because there is nothing more tragic." BEN VEREEN

Ciara was a girl with ambition – determined and driven, yet compassionate and kind. From a young age she wanted to be an accountant and worked her way through primary and secondary school totally focused on her dream. Born in 1970 to Brian and Mary Sullivan,[2] Ciara was the firstborn and in time was joined by one sister and two brothers with whom she got on very well. She was very close to her mother and as Ciara got older they were more like best friends than mother and daughter.

She loved the outdoors and swam, ran and walked, come rain or shine. She had no interest in competitiveness; she just

---

[2] *Names have been changed to protect identities.*

did it because of her love of the outdoors. As a child and young adult, Christmas was Ciara's favourite time of year, closely followed by summer. Although she liked school, Ciara would look forward to summer holidays when she could spend all her time outdoors.

Her parents were quick to tell me that, until the day she died, she never gave them as much as a single minute's trouble. When Ciara decided to move to Dublin at the age of twenty-five to further her studies, her parents knew they would miss her terribly, but they were so proud of her pursuing her dream. They would visit her in Dublin and she would come home every weekend. At heart she was a real home girl and never once missed spending a weekend or Christmas at home with her family. She phoned home every day and she and her mother would often enjoy a "girls' day out" in Dublin. Ciara's mother Mary picks up the story.

In June 1997, Ciara started complaining of back pain and went to the doctor a number of times, each time getting a different diagnosis or treatment. She went away for a week and when she returned she phoned her father and said she was feeling very ill and asked him to come and collect her and take her home. As soon as she got home, we phoned the doctor who came and said he thought it was pneumonia. That was on a Monday and he prescribed strong antibiotics. On Wednesday night we felt she was getting worse instead of better, so we called the doctor back and he referred her to St Vincent's in Dublin. Ciara went up in the ambulance on the Thursday morning and I followed behind in the car.

Ciara was actually delighted at being admitted to hospital because she felt that they would be able to find out what was wrong with her. She had a CT scan on the Tuesday, but no report of this was filed until Wednesday night. She was put on a drug to treat the clot on her lung and was taken for another scan on the Thursday, which showed no evidence of clots, so she was taken off the drugs she was on to treat clots.

Later on, she asked if she could get up and have a shower. She was told she could, so she gathered up her toiletries and set off for the shower. However, she collapsed in the corridor and was taken back to her bed, where she died shortly afterwards. A coroner's post mortem was carried out, which showed she died of a massive pulmonary embolism. When it was performed, we knew nothing about organ retention . . .

(Ciara's mother is too upset to continue, so her father takes over.)

We assumed that after a post mortem everything was put back to how it was when you were born. When they decided to make it a coroner's post mortem, they waited thirty-nine hours before carrying it out. They said they were short-staffed because it was the weekend – but Ciara died on Thursday. When I spoke to the pathologist on the Saturday he said the delay was because the staff wouldn't be available. However, when I saw the death certificate, I saw that it had been signed off by the Chief Profector. We wondered if the decision to wait until the Saturday was to enable students to participate, but we shall never know.

They retained Ciara's brain, even though it was obvious her brain had nothing to do with the cause of death.

Although we tried to make her funeral a celebration of her life, we were devastated and inconsolable. Our beautiful daughter had been taken from us at the prime of her life when she still had so much to do and to offer the world. It didn't seem fair.

We heard about Alder Hey in 1999 when it hit the news. Mary wanted to find out if Ciara had been affected, but initially I didn't. However, after a while I changed my mind and we phoned the hospital. Initially we had great difficulty getting any sort of information from them. I couldn't tell you how many times we phoned and wrote to them. I had to get information under the Freedom of Information Act because the hospital wouldn't co-operate with us. We were going around in circles; they just wouldn't give us a straight answer to a straight question.

Eventually we returned to the hospital for a meeting with the chief pathologist and hospital CEO in attendance. I think there was a social worker there as well. The meeting was very aggravating because they would only speak to partially answer our questions. We weren't aware a coroner's post mortem didn't require consent.

We were told that her brain had been sent to Wales as clinical waste. Then we were told it was sent to a teaching hospital there. We never got any further and to this day we don't know what happened.

We live in a culture that assumes doctors can do what they like and in our case they did what they liked. We are one of the few countries in the Western world to have no human tissue act or law. *The difference between rules and law is that, if you break a rule, you get a slap on the wrist; however, if you break the law, you are punished.* What I want most now is legislation to be enacted that will prevent this from ever happening again. We just want the truth, an apology and recognition that what they did was wrong. We want an assurance it will never again be allowed to happen and until we have legislation in place, we cannot guarantee this.

The Madden Report is a summary of the half-finished Dunne Report and was written only because they had to give something to justify the reported €20 million spent on the Dunne Report. As a report it is of no substance and certainly does not answer any of the questions parents have. I call for the second part of the Dunne Report to be opened as promised by Micheál Martin when he was Minister for Health. *All we want is the truth.*

Note from author: According to the official Madden Report, Ciara wasn't taken into account when calculating figures. Only those born alive and under the age of twelve were.

CHAPTER 8

Glands For Sale

"Power does not corrupt. Fear corrupts . . .
Perhaps the fear of a loss of power."

JOHN STEINBECK

When news began to filter into the public domain about organs being retained by hospitals in the UK, there was naturally concern that the same thing had happened here. What followed was an onslaught of calls to hospitals around the country, asking if the glands and organs of loved ones – and in particular babies and children – had been retained by the hospital. According to the Madden Report, hospitals handled the crisis as follows:

2.5 Our Lady's Hospital for Sick Children, Crumlin

Subsequent to the media attention on the topic of organ retention on 6th December 1999, Crumlin Hospital bore the lion's share of enquiries at that time and in the following two years. It received a total of 706 enquiries, of which 559 had post mortems. Initially the consultant histopathologist at the hospital contacted each family within 24–48 hours and arranged to discuss each individual case with the family concerned, either by telephone where organ retention was not a feature of the case, or by meeting the family (usually within a week of their call) to explain the nature and purpose of a post mortem and the necessity for retention of tissue and organs in their specific case. As a result of the volume of enquiries received by the hospital in the week of 6th December, Crumlin Hospital set up a Patient Support Unit to handle the enquiries it received from parents. The Unit was run by senior administrative staff and supported by a retired clinician, a clinical psychologist, the chaplaincy team and social workers. Other clinical consultants, members of the pathology department and medical records staff gave additional support. Two dedicated help lines were set up and a standard set of questions asked of each enquirer in order to establish the necessary facts. Due to the volume of enquiries, the consultant histopathologist could not meet each family individually and it was decided to refer the enquiries to the original consultant who had treated the child. This usually involved a meeting or telephone contact between the clinician and the family, followed up by written confirmation of the relevant information. Crumlin Hospital states that its intention to provide a full response was hampered by the fact that the pathologist who had worked at the hospital for twenty-eight years was deceased. There was a lack of documentary evidence of practices and procedures, the post-mortem reports rarely recorded the retention of organs unless the central nervous system had been referred to a neuropathologist for expert opinion, and there was also a significant time pressure imposed on staff to respond quickly to enquiries. Due to the lack of information recorded on the reports, the consultant histopathologist used his expertise and experience to interpret the reports to the best of his ability and to form an opinion as to whether or not organs had been retained. Information subsequently came to light in 2000, which caused him to reassess the usefulness of his interpretation of the post-mortem reports in circumstances where he did not have full information of the practices of his deceased predecessor. As a result he decided to discontinue the practice of providing an opinion as to whether or not organs had been retained. As a consequence of the difficulty in ascertaining the relevant information, sometimes information had to be relayed to families on a second occasion, and the hospital acknowledges that the families may have perceived this as a drip-feed of information. Crumlin Hospital was perhaps unique in being the focus of attention for the media and the public in late 1999. Some families believed from inaccurate media reporting that the organ retention was carried out only in Crumlin, that post mortems had been carried out without families' knowledge, and some believed that organs had been used for transplantation without their knowledge. In dealing with the enquiries that were made to the hospital, social workers, clinical nurse specialists, pathologists, medical and support staff had to correct these misapprehensions as well as deal with the distress, hurt and anger caused and support the families who were trying to cope with upsetting information.

2.6 The Rotunda

When the revelations regarding organ retention practices began to be highlighted by the media in late 1999, the Rotunda Hospital confirmed to the Department of Health and Children that it retained tissues from post mortems. In early 2000, the Master issued a statement setting out post-mortem practices and inviting parents to contact a help line. The hospital placed a notice in newspapers in March 2000 inviting contact with the help line and apologising for any hurt caused to families. Calls were directed to the head medical social worker and clinical risk manager. The matron and master's offices also received calls at this time. An ad-hoc multi-disciplinary committee was formed to co-ordinate the hospital's response. The hospital received 240 enquiries up to March 2000. Initial letters were sent to families who had contacted the hospital and arrangements made for them to attend meetings with hospital staff. In some cases families requested meetings with a pathologist and this was facilitated by the hospital. A full-time bereavement support service was provided from July/August 2001.

2.7 The Coombe

The Coombe issued a public statement in February and March 2000 stating that organ retention may be a necessary part of post-mortem examinations, and that subsequent to examination, organs were incinerated by the hospital. The hospital set up a help line in March 2000. It received 130 queries, not all of which are relevant to the terms of reference of this Inquiry. Each telephone call was logged and callers were asked to confirm their query in writing so as to protect confidentiality. Each query was acknowledged in writing and searches were made to identify relevant records. Parents were invited to attend a meeting with a clinician/pathologist.

2.8 National Maternity Hospital, Holles Street

In December 1999/January 2000 the hospital set up a team of fifty individuals to deal with enquiries. This group was drawn from senior staff members from midwifery, management, nursing staff, chaplaincy, and social workers. A clinical psychotherapist was engaged by the hospital to train hospital staff in dealing with the issues that might arise. From January 2000 to April 2002, the hospital dealt with 818 cases where organs had been retained. A full-time bereavement liaison officer was employed by the hospital in September 2001 and works in close contact with social workers and the hospital chaplain to ensure that all bereaved parents are dealt with sensitively. Counselling is provided by the bereavement counselling services at the hospital in conjunction with clinicians.

2.9 Children's University Hospital, Temple Street

Temple Street received 193 enquiries during 2000. Extra staff were employed in the Medical Social Work department to deal with these enquiries. The hospital appointed a medical social worker as post-mortem co-ordinator to co-ordinate the hospital's response to the enquiries. On receipt of an enquiry a social worker contacted a consultant pathologist at the hospital to review the post-mortem report and clinical notes if available. From mid-2000, the practice was altered by facilitating a meeting between the post-mortem inquiry officer and the parents. In addition, the pathologist was available to meet the parents, if required. The hospital established an incident room and a freephone help line to deal with enquiries.

2.10 AMINCH (Tallaght Hospital)

AMINCH state that they first received an enquiry in 1998 relating to post-mortem practices, and dealt with any queries on a case-by-case basis until 2000. Since that year a special projects office has been established to deal with queries and find out the relevant information for families who request it.

Helplines were set up and it wasn't long before it was established that in this widespread practice glands and organs had not only been retained, but in some cases, pituitary glands (located in the centre of the skull, just behind the bridge of the nose, and about the size of a pea) were sold to pharmaceutical companies (see below) – a fact backed up by the Madden Report. Equally outrageous, other organs had been left on shelves or in sheds to the point where they were no good for anything except incineration.

Parents for Justice learned that pituitary glands were sold by hospitals between 1974 and 1986. The glands were sold to pharmaceutical companies to be used in the manufacture of a growth hormone medication for children with stunted growth. This practice was stopped in 1985 because, PFJ were told, the pharmaceutical companies had now made a synthetic form of the medication. However, they later learned that the pharmaceutical companies *had* to make a synthetic form of the medication because a contaminated batch of the medicine had been given to patients who later went on to develop CJD and died.

They learned this through Freedom of Information documents and they also learned that one pharmaceutical company sent a letter to Our Lady's Hospital – of which PFJ have a copy – saying that the collection of pituitary glands *may* resume after a period of time. The families didn't know anything about the fact that these glands were sold or used in this way.

According to the Madden Report: "no consent was obtained for the extraction and supply of pituitary glands. Although motivated to meet the medical needs of children suffering from growth hormone deficiency, this practice was inappropriate without the knowledge and authorisation of the parents and deceased children from whom the glands were removed."

Dr Madden is indeed correct when she cites the practice as being "inappropriate". However, what follows, if proof of payment was ever contested, should vindicate any claim. Chapter 6 Section 8 of the Madden Report is entitled: "Payment for Glands" and reads as follows.

8.1 *Kabi Vitrum (pharmaceutical company) paid a fixed nominal sum for the work involved in the extraction of each pituitary gland. These sums were intended to defray the cost of performing the additional work required during the post mortem to extract, remove and store the pituitary gland.*

8.2 *In 1978 the payment was IR£1.50 per pituitary gland collected. In about November 1981 the payment was increased to IR£2.50, and by 1985 the payment had risen to between IR£3.00 and IR£3.50 for each pituitary gland delivered.*

8.3 *The supply hospitals were often given equipment and tools necessary for the proper removal, treatment and storage of the glands. Where necessary a small, inexpensive deep freezer was supplied for the proper storage of pituitary glands until their collection. In addition, Kabi Vitrum also supplied items such as a histopathologist's lamp and textbooks.*

8.4 *Most hospitals had no documentation relating to the supply of pituitary glands or any payment that may have been received. Some stated they received textbooks or teaching slides. Another stated that payment was made to a research charity. In some hospitals a nominal handling fee was paid to the mortuary technician.*

Hospitals that supplied glands according to the Madden Report:

- Tralee General Hospital
- Our Lady's Hospital, Navan
- Our Lady's Hospital, Drogheda
- Waterford Regional Hospital
- St James's Hospital, Dublin
- Midland Regional Hospital at Mullingar
- Midland Regional Hospital at Tullamore
- Midland Regional Hospital at Portlaoise
- St Joseph's Hospital, Longford
- Mayo General Hospital
- Letterkenny Hospital
- Sligo General Hospital
- Portiuncula Hospital
- Beaumont Hospital, Dublin
- St Laurence's Hospital (services transferred to Beaumont 1987)

- Our Lady's Hospital for Sick Children, Crumlin, Dublin
- Children's University Hospital, Temple Street, Dublin
- National Maternity Hospital, Holles Street, Dublin
- The Coombe Women's Hospital, Dublin
- Cork University Hospital
- St Vincent's Hospital, Dublin
- Galway Regional Hospital
- Limerick Regional Hospital
- St John's Hospital, Limerick
- Barrington's Hospital, Limerick
- North Infirmary, Cork

For most hospitals, it appears that pituitary glands were supplied during the late 1970s to the mid-1980s, though very few hospitals can provide any documentation in this regard.

Hospitals that did not supply glands:

- Blackrock Clinic, Dublin
- Bantry General Hospital
- St Mary's Orthopaedic Hospital, Cork
- Mallow General Hospital
- Rotunda Hospital, Dublin
- Cavan General Hospital
- Monaghan General Hospital
- Erinville Hospital, Cork

- South Infirmary/Victoria Hospital, Cork
- Roscommon Hospital
- Mater Private Hospital, Dublin
- St Columcille's Hospital, Loughlinstown
- Adelaide and Meath Hospital incorporating the National Children's Hospital

Department of Health and Children

According to the Report, although the Department of Health and Children were aware of the distribution of growth hormone in Ireland (since the licence was issued in 1976), no concerns appear to have been voiced by the Department regarding the issue of consent for the extraction and supply of the glands used in the manufacture of this product until 2000.

During his first meeting with Parents for Justice on 9th February 2000 as Minister for Health, their records show that Micheál Martin was horrified when he heard that pituitary glands were being given/sold to pharmaceutical companies. However, when the issue of money came up, Minister Martin said: *"If I find out that even a penny changed hands this puts a completely different slant on things."* Well, Minister Martin knows now and has known for quite some time that many thousands of pennies exchanged hands. The proof is reproduced on the following pages. Names have been blanked out so as not to implicate individuals.

Documents

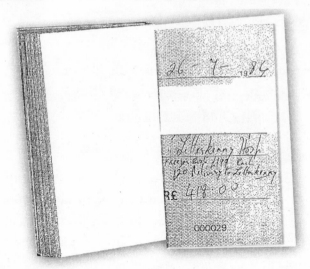

This money was used for freezers in which to store pituitary glands

13th April, 1977.

Antigen Ltd.,
Roscrea,
Co. Tipperary.

Dear

    In reply to your letter of 5th April, your representative may
collect the pituitary glands at any time. She should contact
              at the Mortuary as he will have them ready.

    Would you kindly make the cheque payable to:

    With many thanks,

        Yours sincerely,

Mr.
Letterkenny General Hospital,
Letterkenny,
CO. DONEGAL

EM/A   October 21, 1982

Dear
Many thanks for the pituitary glands which I collected yesterday,
Enclosed herewith cheque for £65 as a gesture for your collaboration.

With renewed thanks.

Kind Regards.

Yours sincerely,

Dictated but not signed

Reads: "Many thanks for the pituitary glands which I collected yesterday. Enclosed herewith cheque for £65 as a gesture for your collaboration." Name of recipient and sender both blanked out.

INTER OFFICE MEMO

CASHEL ROAD, DUBLIN.

DATE: October 21, 1982

TO:

FROM: 1 0254

COPIES:

SUBJECT: COLLECTION OF PITUITARY GLANDS

Please supply cheque in the sum of £65   payable to
Letterkenny General Hospital, in respect
of his collaboration in above and debit Nordisk Insulin
Budget Category 17:009 (pituitaries) accordingly.

INTER OFFICE MEMO

CASHEL ROAD, DUBLIN.

0207

L E O

76

DATE: June 30, 1983

TO:

FROM:

COPIES:

SUBJECT: COLLECTION OF PITUITARY GLANDS

Please supply the following cheques in respect of above
and debit Nordisk 17,009 (pituitaries)

Letterkenny   General   £37.50

OUR LADY'S HOSPITAL FOR SICK CHILDREN

TELEPHONE: 490 6100   FAX 495 8873

CRUMLIN
DUBLIN 12

12 June 2001

Private & Confidential

Pharmacia Ireland Limited
Airways Industrial Estate
Dublin 17

Re: **Pituitary Glands**

Dear

It has just been brought to our attention that you may have been able to provide patient identity for the source of some pituitary glands provided to Kabi Vitrum from Galway Regional Hospital.

I would appreciate if you could confirm whether you have any more information to allow you to identify sources of pituitary glands collected here at Our Lady's Hospital for Sick Children, Crumlin during the period of 1974 to 1985.

Yours sincerely

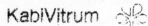

KabiVitrum

Dr Cand... No. ... ...
PO Box 50
Chapelizod
Dublin 20
Republic of Ireland
Telephone Dublin 266 661/266 661

Our Lady's Hospital for Sick Children,
Crumlin,
Dublin 12.

Dear

Many thanks for the 35 Pituitary Glands which were collected from your
department by me recently. As in the past I enclose a cheque in favour
of the Childrens Research Centre. The amount involved on this occasion
is £52.50. I hope this is in order for you.

From now onwards the amount payable for the work involved in the extraction
of the glands will be raised by £1 to a contribution of £2.50 to take account
of inflation etc.,

May I take this opportunity to wish you a very happy Christmas and I look
forward to seeing you early in 1982.

Registered Office
KabiVitrum Ltd
Kilton House
Uxbridge Road

Telephones
01-567 4717/8
01-579 1871/3

Telex
936109 Kabluk G

Registered
England No 696326

Human Remains and Body Parts Policy on eBay

When one thinks of eBay, one thinks of counterfeit handbags and designer goods. It was with great shock that I read their disclaimer about the sale and purchase of body parts on their site . . .

Humans, the human body, or any human body parts are not permitted on eBay. Items that contain human hair (such as lockets) as well as skulls and skeletons that are used for medical purposes may be listed on eBay. eBay does not permit the sale of Native American skulls, bones or other Native American grave-related items, as the sale of such items may violate federal law.

Violations of this policy may result in a range of actions, including:

- *Listing cancellation*
- *Limits on account privileges*
- *Account suspension*
- *Forfeit of eBay fees on cancelled listings*
- *Loss of PowerSeller status*

Examples of prohibited items include, but are not limited to:

- *organs*
- *bone*
- *blood*
- *waste*
- *sperm*
- *eggs*

(Source: Ebay – http://pages.ebay.com/help/policies/remains.html)

CHAPTER 9

Ann's Story:
Everlasting Love

"Death leaves a heartache no one can heal, love leaves a memory no one can steal."

FROM A HEADSTONE IN IRELAND

Tommy was a man who couldn't sit still. Although he was a quiet and shy man, he worked hard and was a terrific husband and father. His passion was cars and he would spend hours under the bonnets of various cars tinkering around. His wife, Ann, would often come home to find the engine of a car on the kitchen floor. Tommy was also a dab hand at DIY and added an extension to the house. He hated doing nothing and was constantly going around the house looking for things to do. Tommy and Ann had six children, now ranging in age from forty-three to twins of thirty. Life in the Docherty household was never dull and as a family, they enjoyed many family days out and trips to the country.

161

Tommy taught the children many things, but above all he taught them loyalty and how important it was to be loyal to people. Ann freely admits she was the disciplinarian and all the kids knew that what they couldn't get from Ann they'd only have to ask Dad. They were twenty-eight years married when Tommy died and Ann says they were as happy the day he died as they were on their wedding day. Ann takes up the story . . .

Our children are a credit to him and the loyalty he instilled in them has stood to all of them. Tommy used to love fishing and one of his favourite places to fish was in Donegal. It's hard to describe Tommy physically; I suppose he was of average build and average height. He could be very dry at times and had a caustic sense of humour.

We met in London. I went over in February 1963 to a friend of mine who was working in Fleet Street and I got a job in an advertising agency. We shared a bedsit and Tommy and his two brothers lived upstairs. We started going out in March; by Christmas we were engaged and by Christmas 1964 we were married. Tommy always supported me in everything I wanted to do. Our first son was born in London in 1965 and we returned to Ireland in September 1966. We decided to return home because I wanted to. Our son was still young and if things didn't work out we could still return to London. The next twenty-eight years were spent with the usual ups and downs of family life.

In January 1992 Tommy went into hospital for a simple operation to unblock an artery in his leg. All went well and the operation was repeated in June 1992. On the day he was due to have the surgery, 30th June, the operation was cancelled because the theatre was needed for an emergency. However, it was to go ahead the following day, 1st July. Well, it didn't go ahead, because Tommy died in theatre before the operation began. His sudden death was hard to cope with; I got a call from the hospital to say things weren't going well and could I come down and bring someone with me. I knew the moment I got there; he was still in the theatre. Most of the family were there by then and we said prayers. It was so surreal.

Ann discovered he had been given a penicillin-based drug called Augmentin to which he was allergic. This was clearly marked on his notes at least four times. However, there were other charts that stated NKA (No Known Allergies).

Tommy died in July, the inquest was held in December and Ann finally got to see his notes the following February. Ann was told Tommy's brain had been retained and incinerated. Due to the fact that evidence and the full post mortem report and conclusion were withheld from the inquest, Ann was granted a second inquest by the Attorney-General.

The Coroner fought the Attorney-General decision up to the Supreme Court. The High Court said he was right, but the Supreme Court disagreed. The second inquiry never went ahead because, allegedly, there was no new evidence – even though there was evidence and documentation that was not presented at the original hearing. Ann is adamant this constituted new evidence and fought and fought for the second inquiry. However, sadly she was fighting a system in which Tommy was just another unfortunate statistic.

CHAPTER 10

With a Little Help from the Professionals

"Show me the manner in which a nation cares for its dead, and I will measure with mathematical exactness the tender mercies of its peoples, their loyalty to high ideals and their regard for the laws of the land."

WILLIAM EWART GLADSTONE

The organ retention scandal can be a very confusing and complicated issue if you are not familiar with the events, the background and indeed the terminology. Like most people, I knew absolutely nothing about organ retention prior to my son's organs being retained and until eleven years after his death. To me, organ retention was something like organ donation. As it didn't particularly affect me, I didn't go out of my way to learn about it.

My only involvement with organs was to carry a donor card, which is something I still do and recommend highly to people. However, I soon realised just how little I knew about the scandal when I became caught up in it. It has been a decade since the scandal broke in Ireland

and I am still learning new things about it. At the start I couldn't have imagined the complexities I would face and some of the decisions I would be forced to make.

Medical terminology is unlike everyday English and I had to take a crash course in trying to understand as much of it as I could as quickly as possible. In this book I have tried to avoid the usage of medical terminology as much as possible, but with a book such as this, it would be impossible to completely avoid it. Then, of course, I had to find out who did what and where to find them and what certain abbreviations meant and why one department was different from another and what each department did and who was responsible for what. It was a learning curve of epic proportion. Every time I felt I knew all there was to know, something else would crop up.

It would be easy for me to be bitter and cynical about this scandal, but this would do little except eat away at me and be counter-productive. Instead I chose to first learn what I was dealing with and then to do something about it. It's always easier to deal with something when you know as much as you can about it. As I knew absolutely nothing, I started at the beginning and took it from there.

I do not claim to be an expert and I certainly don't claim to know everything. However, I do know a lot more than I did when I first started my journey and I hope that sharing what I know will make it a little easier for you to understand what the organ retention scandal is really about and why it has raged on for so long, making history in the process. The first thing I did was go to the experts, and this chapter features many of their words and explanations.

Medical Jargon

When reading about autopsies/organ retention, etc., there are many different medical procedures and references that you may hear about. Some you will understand, others you may not. It would be impossible to list every single procedure in a single chapter; however, I will list some of the most common terms and references you are likely to come across. I would like to take this opportunity to thank St James's Hospital, Dublin for their kind assistance with compiling this section. As a lay person, it would have been difficult to convey accurate information – which is exactly the reason why you have to understand it.

Post Mortem/Autopsy – An Explanation

"Necropsy" is from the Greek for "seeing a dead body". According to Dr Karl Kruszelnicki, the first recorded autopsies were carried out around 300 BC by doctors living in Alexandria. Some 500 years later, in 200 AD, medicine had advanced. The Greek doctor Galen actually compared what he found at autopsy with what he had seen on his patients and what they had complained of. The first known legal autopsy, to try to find the cause of death, was ordered by a magistrate in Bologna in 1302. It is not widely known that, in order to understand the human anatomy better and to improve their skills, the artists Leonardo da Vinci and Michelangelo each performed autopsies. "The Anatomy

Lesson of Dr Nicolaes Tulp" is a famous painting by Rembrandt, depicting an autopsy.

However, the autopsy really became significant in 1761, when Giovanni Morgagni published his great work, *On the Seats and Causes of Diseases as Investigated by Anatomy*. Morgagni (1682–1771) is considered to be the intellectual founder of autopsy and is celebrated as the father of modern anatomical pathology.

Ireland's first professor of pathology was Edmund Joseph McWeeney (1864–1925). He was born in Dublin and was the third son of Theophilus Joseph and Margaret Kendallen. His father was a journalist. They lived in Heytesbury Street, Dublin. Edmund was professor of pathology in the Catholic University School of Medicine before moving to University College Dublin (UCD) upon its inception in 1908.

Autopsy
There are two kinds of post mortems; one needs permission from the next of kin and the other does not.

The Coroner's Autopsy
The coroner is an independent official with responsibility under the law for the medico-legal investigation of certain deaths. Permission is not required for a coroner's autopsy. A coroner must inquire into the circumstances of sudden, unexplained, violent or unnatural deaths. This may require an autopsy, sometimes followed by an inquest. The coroner's inquiry is concerned with establishing whether or not the death was due to natural or unnatural causes. If a death was

due to unnatural causes, then an inquest must be held by law.

Deaths occurring under a wide range of conditions must be reported to the coroner, who then inquires into the circumstances of the death. Sometimes a doctor may be in a position to certify the cause of death. If this is so, and if there are no other circumstances requiring investigation, the coroner will permit the doctor to complete a medical certificate of the cause of death, and the death will be registered accordingly. However, if the certificate cannot be completed, the coroner will order that an autopsy be carried out. When the coroner's investigations are completed, the findings of the autopsy may be discussed at hospital meetings in a confidential manner (the deceased's name will not be disclosed).

For a coroner's autopsy, a final report is prepared. This includes all the information from the autopsy and gives the cause of death. This report usually takes between two and eight weeks but it may take much longer if special tests are required. The coroner may then issue a certificate, which allows the registrar of deaths to issue a death certificate. In certain circumstances, the coroner, before issuing a certificate, may order an inquest, which is a hearing of all the evidence about a person's death.

I spoke at length with Denis Cusack, President of the Coroners' Society and also Kildare County Coroner; like so many others, he maintains that the Madden Report has *not* been implemented. "Where are we going to get funding to produce a booklet to assist parents/bereaved relatives and explain our role and what we do, when we hardly have enough funding as it is?" he asked. I asked ten years ago for such a booklet to be introduced, but of course, there were more important things on the agenda. In 2000, PFJ again pushed for such an information leaflet and they received the full support of the Coroner's Report. Dr Cusack continued: "Coroners felt it necessary that the leaflet was developed, *as a matter of urgency*, for family or those who had lost loved ones. We believe it is the right of the family to be fully informed, particularly in the case of organ retention for the past ten years – these requests were listed in terms of immediate urgency all those years ago . . ."

"What must be remembered about the Madden Report is *that it is based only on recommendations, not law*," says Cusack, who got fed up waiting for things to happen, so he set up his own website. "I would like to acknowledge that this would not have been possible without funding from Kildare County Council," he acknowledged. Kildare has been very proactive in the absence of legislation. Quite a number of coroners now have in place designated persons in the case of organ retention because they know how traumatic it can be for a family. A number of coroners have websites explaining everything; there are a small number who do not – not because they wouldn't like to, but due to a lack of resources.

From speaking with Dr Denis Cusack, I get the impression that he is a man both dedicated to his work and, moreover, dedicated to the deceased and those left behind. He is a compassionate man who is easy to talk to and was only too willing to answer my questions without hesitation.

Sandra Smith, Head of Coroner Service Information Team, works very closely with the Coroners' Society. She has suggested the distribution of a nationwide booklet that could simply have the relevant county inserted in it. When I asked Dr Cusack what three things he would immediately bring in, he replied:

- Bring forward tissue legislation

- Bring in faculty pathologists

- A Coroners Bill 2008 (The Bill is currently awaiting report stage in the Dáil, having completed committee stage on 11 November, 2008.)

Dr Cusack continues:

We are not going to wait for legislation. In the interim we plan to improve channels of communication and information. The purpose of the website is to give citizens informed information – and also an overview of the law and the procedure. With a coroner's report permission from next of kin is not sought, whereas in a hospital it is.

We work in a legal process. We work in a legal framework with passion and sensibility. Our report goes to the family doctor in a sealed enveloped within a sealed envelope because not all families choose that moment to find out what happened their loved one. For some it can take weeks or even months.

Dublin City Coroner Dr Brian Farrell also set up a website, details of which are listed in the information section. The site is very informative and certainly worth a look for those interested in knowing more about the role of a coroner. Dr Farrell was only too happy to comply with the Dunne Report and supplied whatever documents he was asked for.

The Hospital Autopsy

If the coroner decides that a coroner's autopsy is not required, or if it was not necessary to report the death to the coroner, the deceased's doctors may request a hospital autopsy. The autopsy or post-mortem examination gives information on the organs and systems of the body and shows by direct vision and by microscopic examination what damage has been caused by disease. It's often possible to get more details of the illness than has been learned from a series of examinations done before death. This allows a more complete assessment of a patient's illness, of the response to treatment and of the cause of death. However, the autopsy may not answer all questions and in some cases may fail to show the cause of death.

For a hospital autopsy, the pathologist discusses the findings with the patient's consultant and then issues a final report, usually four to eight weeks following the autopsy. The findings of the autopsy may be discussed at hospital meetings in a confidential manner (the deceased's name will not be disclosed). The next of kin may obtain a copy of the pathologist's report, either directly or through their own general practitioner, and may make arrangements to discuss the findings with the deceased's consultant or with the pathologist.

Benefits of an Autopsy

For the bereaved family the autopsy not only provides information and explanations on the illness and cause of death but also may reveal co-existing conditions including inherited diseases, the early recognition of which may be of benefit to other family members. New diseases are often first recognised by autopsy – for instance, the new variant of CJD (Creutzfeldt-Jakob Disease), which was in the news because of its association with "mad cow disease", was defined by post-mortem studies.

Family members are often comforted by the knowledge that their loved one's death, through the autopsy, can advance medical knowledge and help others by contributing to the fight against disease. This is one of the reasons parents of children whose organs had been retained had this opportunity taken away from them, on top of everything else.

Bereavement Counsellors

Most hospitals now have designated bereavement counsellors attached to the social work department who are available to help with all aspects of bereavement. If required they will explain details of the autopsy, and organ retention, death certificates and funeral arrangements. Relatives will usually be contacted by bereavement counsellors in the period shortly after death.

While some people want to know every last detail, there are others who don't want to know anything. People react differently to grief and it is very important to know that there is no wrong or right way. Grief doesn't always manifest itself immediately; sometimes it can take weeks or even months. There are some very helpful websites on bereavement counselling which I have listed at the back of this book; a particularly good one is: www.citizensinformation.ie/categories/death (*bereavement counselling and support*).

Emotions play a big part of grief and although you may think you are okay, you would be surprised how much it would help to talk to someone. All the hospitals have specially trained people for this. Equally you may find yourself lashing out or retreating into yourself. There are many places from which you can source information. However tempting the internet may be, my advice is to talk to a trained nurse or counsellor first. The internet is largely uncensored and it is very easy to come across information and images that you will never forget.

The Death Certificate

Where a coroner's autopsy has been performed, the death will be registered when the coroner issues a coroner's certificate on receipt of the final autopsy report. Where a hospital autopsy has been performed, the doctor who attended the deceased certifies the cause of death. A coroner's autopsy report may be obtained in time.

Death certificates may be applied for online at www.groireland.ie and cost €10, which includes postage and packing, or by calling in person to: Civil Registration Office, Joyce House, 8/11 Lombard Street East, Dublin 2 (opening hours: 9.30 a.m. – 4.30 p.m.).

Mortuary

This is the place where the body of the deceased is stored and is usually where a post mortem takes place, which is performed by a pathologist.

Pathologist

A pathologist is a qualified doctor who has completed a minimum of six years' medical training and has gone on and completed an additional five years' pathology training. All hospitals have a pathology department, which is run by a pathologist and his or her team. One of the primary functions of a pathologist is to establish the cause of death by examining the body. This is done in a number of ways, but most commonly by opening the body by cutting a T-shape incision and examining the organs one by one before replacing them. Some causes of death and disease are easier to identify than others. Often it is only possible to determine a disease internally as there is no visible trace of it externally.

Organ Donation

Organ donation for transplant purpose is when living organs are donated by the donor or the donor's family for transplant use in order to save lives. This experience has proved to be a very positive one for both families. There are many cases of donor exchange in families, where one family member is compatible with the person needing a kidney. The human body can function perfectly well with only one kidney. Those who wish to donate their organs after their death usually carry a donor card, which is signed by them and their next of kin.

Mark Murphy, CEO of the Irish Kidney Association told me that my request was the *first time he had been asked to comment on the unauthorised retention of organs in Ireland*. I was rather shocked by this, given that Ireland has been in the grip of an organ retention scandal for the past decade. However, I got on with the job in hand and found him very affable and more than willing to answer my questions and give his own opinion. Actually, throughout my research for this book, people were very to happy to give an opinion or suggestion. It was as if they had never before been asked or had a platform in which they could air their views.

Mark Murphy, Irish Kidney Association (IKA)

Unfortunately, it is at a time of intense grief that the intrusion of various personnel takes place. Sadly there is no other time to do it, and in particular, time is of the essence if organ donation is going to take place, explains Mark Murphy, CEO, IKA.

We in the Irish Kidney Association are in the position that we are asking the public to consider offering their organs after death to someone who could use them in transplantation. What was discovered was that a certain section of the medical profession were collecting organs without permission. This did undermine our delicate position with the public because they don't distinguish between sections in the medical profession.

The IKA received many phone calls asking for clarification between organs for transplantation and organs for retention. This was hard to explain in simple terms. At the time about fifty of our dialysis and transplanted patients were in the centre of the Hepatitis C scandal, which directly affected them. About twenty of them are still alive. That scandal shortened people's lives. The organ retention scandal slowed down donation, which directly affects organ transplantation, which extends people's lives.

The organ retention scandal showed up the lack of governance of the medical profession. It made me examine the governance of organ donation for transplantation – which I discovered is equally lacking in Ireland. The Minister has recently promised to improve this.

The shared similarity between the two scandals – organ retention and Hep C – is the complete arrogance of individuals within the medical profession working in an uncontrolled, unsupervised environment. The other medical professionals were horrified at their colleagues' attitudes, but did little, if anything, to rectify the public mistrust of the profession in total.

My renal patients all rely on the skills of various sections of the medical profession for their future health – as do so many other patients – and they would always choose "not to rock the boat". This shows the vulnerability of all chronic patients who rely for their future on the skills of doctors.

Parents of deceased children whose organs were retained may never get answers or closure. Families of organ donors know that some people's lives have been extended and saved by their decision to donate their deceased relatives' organs. If only parents had been asked permission to retain their children's organs, they might also have found some comfort in their loss – as organ donors' families do. This is the "tragedy" that could have so easily been averted. They weren't asked and the whole medical community is affected by mistrust again – caused by another section of their profession. I think the only way forward now is by the opt in/out option currently being debated.

What may not be widely known is that today in Ireland there are over 2,400 recipients of kidney transplants – the youngest is just four years old and the oldest is eighty years old. The longest surviving transplant is thirty-seven years and is still going strong today. The first transplant was carried out here in 1967 and since then there have been well over 3,000 kidney transplants carried out.

Opt In/Out Bill

Again, I knew very little about the opt in/out bill when I first heard about it, but I understand it a little better now that I have done some research on it. Different countries have different laws governing organ donation, which is different from human tissue legislation, which I will explain after opt in/out. The following options are being proposed by Government.

Public Consultation: Consent for the Donation of Organs after Death for Transplantation
The Government has approved the preparation of the General Scheme and Heads of a Human Tissue Bill to regulate the removal, retention, storage, use and disposal of human tissue from deceased persons and related matters, including the issue of

consent for donation of organs after death for transplantation. As part of this process, the Department has been asked to examine the case for the "opt-in", "opt-out" and "mandated choice" systems of consent for organ donation.

(Option A) Opt-out – *sometimes called* **presumed consent**
The person is presumed to have consented to donate his or her organs after death unless he or she has specified otherwise.

(Option B) Opt-in – *sometimes called* **explicit consent**
The person can decide in advance to consent to donate his or her organs, or to nominate someone to make the decision on his/her behalf after death. Where the deceased has not made a decision, his or her family may do so.

(Option C) *Mandated choice and required request*
People would be required by law to specify whether or not they wish to donate their organs after death. This could be done at specified times such as when applying for a State service or benefit or indeed a driving licence, motor tax or passport. The provision of the service or benefit would not be dependent on the choice made. If a person is a potential organ donor, "required request" means that the person's wishes, or their family's, must be ascertained before death, for example in a hospital A & E Department or Intensive Care Unit.

Consent for Organ Donation

OPTION		DESCRIPTION
Option A **Opt-out** *Sometimes called presumed consent* The person is presumed to have consented to donate his/her organs unless he/she has specified otherwise.	**A1. Hard opt-out system** *without exemption*	Doctors can remove organs from every adult who dies – unless a person has registered to opt out. This applies even if relatives know that the deceased would object to donation but had failed to register during life. *Example: Austria.*
	A2. Hard opt-out system *with provision for exemptions*	Doctors can remove organs from every adult who dies – unless a person has registered to opt out **OR** the person belongs to a group that is defined in law as being against an opt-out system. *Example: Singapore, where Muslims chose to opt out as a group.*
	A3. Soft opt-out *without family consultation*	Doctors can remove organs from every adult who dies – unless a person has registered to opt out **OR** the person's relatives tell doctors not to take organs. It is up to the relatives to tell the doctors because the doctors may not ask them. *Example: Belgium.*

OPTION		DESCRIPTION
Option A *Continued*	**A4. Soft opt-out** *with family consultation*	Doctors can remove organs from every adult who dies – unless a person has registered to opt out. It is good practice for doctors to ask the relatives for their agreement at the time of death. *Example: Spain.*
Option B **Opt-in** *Sometimes called explicit consent* The person can decide in advance to consent, or to nominate someone to make the decision on his/her behalf after death. Where the deceased has not made a decision his or her family may do so.	**B1. Soft opt-in system** *with family veto*	Doctors can remove organs from adults who have opted in. It is up to each person to decide if they want to opt in. It is normal practice to let relatives know if the person has opted in and doctors will not proceed if faced with opposition from relatives. *Example: Ireland.*
	B2. Soft opt-in system *with family consultation*	Doctors can remove organs from adults who have opted in. It is up to each person to decide if they want to opt in. It is normal practice to let relatives know if the person has opted in and doctors can decide not to proceed if faced with opposition from relatives, although they have the legal entitlement to proceed according to the individual's wishes. *Example: UK.*

OPTION		DESCRIPTION
Option B *Continued*	**B3. Hard opt-in system** ***without family consultation***	Doctors can remove organs from adults who have opted in. It is up to each person to decide if they want to opt in. Relatives are not able to oppose the person's wishes.
Option C **Mandated choice / required consent** A system of mandated choice would require people to exercise a choice whether or not to donate.	**C1. Soft mandated choice system**	People *are asked to* register their choice to opt in or opt out at specified points and CAN choose whether to do so or not.
	C2. Hard mandated choice system	People *are asked to* register their choice to opt in or opt out at specified points and MUST choose one option.
	C3. Required request	A system of required request would require that a person's wishes MUST be determined before death. Potential donors are identified in hospital Accident and Emergency Departments and Intensive Care Units and the individual or his/her family must be approached and their wishes in relation to organ donation determined.

Human Tissue Legislation

There are only two countries in the Western world without human tissue legislation – Ireland is one and Malta is the other. When I took this matter up with the Department of Health and Children, their reply was comprehensive, if a little confusing at first glance. However, as legislation is one of the two things PFJ has been campaigning for, and indeed something I myself have requested, as have many TDs, it is undoubtedly a step in the right direction, albeit a step that has taken a decade to make. The Department's reply is as follows.

On 23rd September 2008, the Government approved the preparation of the General Scheme and Heads of a Human Tissue Bill to regulate the removal, retention, storage, use and disposal of human tissue from deceased persons and consent for the use of donated tissue from living persons for the purpose of transplantation and research.

The proposed legislation will address hospital post-mortems, which are voluntary procedures, as distinct from coroners' post-mortems which are part of the legal process of determining death and which come within the ambit of the Coroners Act 1962 (to be replaced by the Coroners Bill 2007, which is currently before the Seanad).

Policy context: the discovery that post-mortems had been performed and organs retained without permission. These matters were documented by

Dr Deirdre Madden in her Report into Post-Mortem Practice and Procedures (Madden Report).

Primary purpose: *to implement the key recommendation of the Madden Report that no hospital post-mortem examination should be carried out and no tissue retained for any purpose whatsoever without authorisation.*

Consent/authorisation to be the defining principle underpinning any of the specified activities involving human tissue – post-mortem examination, anatomical examination, public display, transplantation, research, import/export of human tissue from deceased donors. Other principles to be enshrined in the legislation are:

- *Protection of the bodily integrity of the individual before and after death;*

- *Respect for the autonomy of the individual and the rights of the bereaved;*

- *Promotion of the public health benefits of post mortem examination and tissue donation.*

Other provisions in the Bill, although not addressed in the Madden Report, are necessary to provide comprehensive protection for the rights of the tissue donor, whether living or deceased:

- *Provisions on anatomical examination, public display and import/export of human tissue from deceased donors;*

184

- *Consent procedures for use of tissue from deceased donors for research and transplantation;*

- *Consent procedures for use of tissue from living donors for research and transplantation, to avoid the anomaly of providing a greater degree of legal protection to the deceased than to the living;*

- *Prohibition on the commercialisation of human tissue for transplantation.*

Regulatory functions will be assigned to an existing agency. Bill will address consent for retention of human tissue once the Coroner has concluded his investigations. This will complement the provisions in the coroners Bill 2007, which, over two years later, is awaiting Committee Stage in Seanad. The Bill will provide proportionate penalties for breach of its provisions.

This was proving rather a lot of information to digest at speed, but there was more to come.

Human tissue from living and deceased donors, when intended for human application, is regulated in all EU member states by the Directives on the Safety and Quality of Tissues and Cells. The Directives have been transposed into Irish law by the following statutory instruments: SI No. 158 of 2006: European Communities (Quality and Safety of Human Tissues and Cells) Regulations 2006 which transposed Council Directive 2004/23/EC and Commission Directive 2006/17/EC. SI No. 598 of 2007: European Communities (Human Tissues and Cells Traceability Requirements, Notification of Serious Adverse Reactions and Events and Certain Technical Requirements) Regulations 2007 which transposed Commission Directive 2006/86/EC).

Forensic or medico-legal post-mortem examinations, which by definition have a statutory basis, are regulated in this country by means of the Coroners Acts 1962–2005. Many countries also have legislation on transplantation from deceased donors, some have combined this with legislation on all aspects of human tissue use, for example the UK, while others have legislated separately on organ and tissue donation or on donation to schools of anatomy. We have no specific information in relation to legislation across Europe on other aspects of human tissue regulation, for example in relation to non-coroners' post-mortem practice.

Well, I wanted information and in fairness to the DoHC Press Office, the lady I was dealing with went out of her way to assist me. However, try as I might, I could not find what I was looking for within the information that she had given to me. I waded through the text a number of times and decided that either I had missed something completely or my initial question had not been answered in the reply. I decided to use a more direct, but polite approach and kept it short and very much to the point.

Thank you for such a prompt answer, it is appreciated. Although informative, as far as I can ascertain it does not answer my question: Does Ireland have a human tissue legislation act?

The reply contained the information I originally requested and better still, it comprised only a couple of lines.

Ireland does not currently have a human tissue Act. Work is currently underway at drafting the General Scheme of a Human Tissue Bill, which will be submitted to Government when completed and subject to their approval will form the basis of a human tissue bill.

However, the information went on to explain how other countries dealt with the legislation. Although meant to be helpful, and of this I am sure, it made me feel that it was trying to compensate for the fact Ireland has no legislation.

Human tissue regulation has many different facets and has been legislated for in many different ways. It is impossible to state categorically that every country has or does not have legislation covering each of these different facets. Even within the United Kingdom there are two Human Tissue

Acts, one in Scotland and one in England, Wales and Northern Ireland, and there would be some differences in scope between both Acts. In Australia and New Zealand their Human Tissue Acts contain a broadly similar scope to the UK legislation, but many countries have different laws addressing different aspects of human tissue use, e.g. laws specific to anatomy or to transplantation and may well have no legislation in other areas.

I get the feeling we will not see it enacted anytime soon.

Irish Medical Organisation (IMO)

Martin Daly, President of the IMO, was more than happy to answer my questions and said that without doubt lessons had been learned since the scandal broke in 1999.

1   Do you think the medical profession was unfairly portrayed as a group when the scandal broke?

In a general sense when the scandal broke I think it is reasonable to say that the general perception it created was that of doctors having a paternalistic manner. Retrospectively, we were insensitive. In hindsight that type of behaviour would not be tenable today.

Our view as with a lot of scandals in the past ten to fifteen years in relation to all aspects of society, is that lessons must be learned from the outcomes, the reports and the enquiries. I believe with the medical profession now there is far greater public awareness and transparency.

2   What are your own personal views on the scandal?

The idea that any group of professionals, especially those in such a caring profession, should be witness to great personal tragedy and difficulties is terrible for everyone. I think much better standards of communication have been fostered and maintained. That any doctor can act unilaterally, no matter how well intentioned or not, this type of culture is not acceptable any more. The biggest lesson in the medical sense is the era where it was the accepted norm that "doctor knew best" is gone. Now doctors tend to foster relationships with their patients from the cradle to the grave, so to speak!

3   What should be put in place to prevent a recurrence?

There needs to be proper governance in all aspects of patient care – governance written by audit with impartial input. The Medical Council is addressing lay representation at the moment.

4   What lessons have been learned?

A number of lessons have been learned. There is now far greater respect for patients' rights; informed consent has risen dramatically whereby now a patient is fully aware of his or her rights, treatments and options. The protocol governing the whole aspect of consent and information around organ retention has led to better communication with the regulating authority, the General Medical Council.

Dr Deirdre Madden
Below are the questions I asked Dr Madden; her answers follow.

1   What do you think is the single most important thing to come out of the Madden Report?

2   Do you think the Madden Report was given enough time to complete its findings – Anne Dunne had years; you had six months. Surely with such a limited time frame there are pivotal things you missed?

3   What made you decide to base your report on children *"who were born alive and under the age of twelve"* when it is well-documented (including the Geneva Convention) this is not the case?

4   How did you feel taking over from Anne Dunne with such a mammoth task ahead of

you? After all, you had only a few months to complete what had taken her years?

5 Did you continue in private practice while compiling the Madden Report?

6 Retrospectively, are there things you feel you should have included in the report, but elected not to?

7 What was the worst finding of the report for you?

8 What must people learn from the organ retention scandal?

9 What has changed most since the scandal broke?

10 Can you in just a line or two explain the difference between organ retention and organ donation and why they need not worry unduly anymore?

Dear Karina,
I cannot answer all of your questions but in answer to some of them:

1 and 8. I think the most important lesson to be learned from the controversy is the consequences of the failure to communicate with families about post mortem practice which led to huge distress and a breakdown in trust with the medical profession and hospitals. Modern medical practice should be based on openness, respect and partnership with patients and families which would ensure better access to information and choices. Medical education and training should include more teaching of communication skills and professional ethics.

5. I have not been in private practice since the early '90s. I am employed full-time by University College Cork as a lecturer in law.

10. From a medical point of view, organs are removed and retained primarily to provide a comprehensive diagnosis of death. Secondary uses of retained organs include audit, quality assurance, research, education and training, all of which are essential to the provision of medical services to the highest standards.

Organ donation is carried out in accordance with the wishes of the deceased (where known) and the deceased's family in order to provide life-saving treatment to another patient.

The Department of Health and Children is currently preparing a Human Tissue Bill which I understand will deal with many of the issues raised in the report and will provide for the first time in Ireland a legislative base for the authorisation of post mortem practices. This should reassure the public that the concerns expressed in the report have been dealt with.

Best wishes

Deirdre

The Irish Nurses Organisation (INO)

The INO were horrified by the scandal and were happy to air their views on the matter. They said they admired my courage for writing this book, though I don't feel at all courageous. I just feel a sense of profuse sadness – that so much pain and so much trauma could have been so easily avoided, if somebody in the right position had had the courage to speak out and act long ago. That would have been courageous. The mothers who formed Parents for Justice are courageous. In fact, I consider the INO courageous for speaking out so openly about the scandal, but why wouldn't they? They have nothing to hide and were as appalled as the rest of the country. This is their statement, which General Secretary Liam Doran gave to me. I think it eloquently describes the feelings of most.

While medical research is an essential part of learning, for the science of healthcare, nothing excuses or explains the actions of a small minority of well-intentioned people with regard to the organ retention of small babies without the knowledge and agreement of the baby's parents.

I doubt if any of us, on a human personal level, can begin to imagine the sense of hurt, loss and pure sadness that these parents have experienced. This regretful, unforgivable event must never be repeated, regardless of the need of medical science, and parents must always be consulted and fully involved in everything that is being considered with regard to their loving infant.

Responses from Hospitals

Our Lady's Hospital, Crumlin

I would like to thank Lorcan Birthistle, Chief Executive of Our Lady's, for answering all my questions' knowing his busy schedule and lack of spare time.

1   What lessons have been learned as a result of the organ retention scandal?

Our Lady's introduced new consent and information practices surrounding post mortems in 1999, anticipating recommendations on the subject from professional bodies which followed publicity in Ireland later that same year. These processes have continued to evolve in the intervening years, largely in response to observations received from bereaved parents and hospital staff about their effectiveness and appropriateness.

2   What new practices have been implemented as a result?

The new consent and information procedures broadly reflect national guidelines. However, in Our Lady's, the pathologist meets each family prior to the procedure to explain both the details of the examination and to assist the family with appropriate funeral arrangements. The pathologist therefore completes all the necessary documentation including consent forms, a practice that is unusual in other hospitals. However, we have found that this mechanism leads to greater clarity for family and pathologist about the planned procedure and has been well received. The hospital has published its experience with this practice in the British Medical Journal.

3   Do you have liaison nurses on the staff to deal specifically with bereaved parents?

Bereaved parents are assisted by multi-disciplinary teams rather than an individual bereavement liaison nurse. Many of the individuals involved in these teams would overlap with the staff who cared for the child prior to death, an arrangement which we believe gives greater continuity. Given the central role of the pathologist in discussing post mortem and funeral arrangements, the role for a full-time bereavement liaison nurse at Our Lady's would be very different from that in other hospitals. Nonetheless, the Death, Dying and Bereavement Committee of the hospital, a committee which includes bereaved parents, continue to review and update all hospital practices in this area and is currently working with the Hospice Foundation about the possible establishment of a bereavement co-ordinator post for terminally ill children.

4   How would you deal in the event of someone ringing up asking if their child's organs were still there?

The hospital Patient Services Department follow guidelines developed in the HSE for any such enquiries.

5   Who would deal with that person and what options would they be given?

The hospital follows guidelines developed in the HSE for any such enquiries.

6   Do you have leaflets/information on organ retention/bereavement?

The hospital has a range of information on post mortem practice, the death of a child and bereavement. The Death, Dying and Bereavement Committee continue to review this area.

7   What options do parents have if organs are still at the hospital?

The hospital follows guidelines developed in the HSE for any such enquiries.

8   Who would attend a meeting with them to answer/address any questions they may have?

Representatives from the relevant multidisciplinary team involved in the care of the child would attend these meetings.

9   Is a memorial service held at the hospital and do you assist parents with burial arrangements of their choosing?

The Death Dying and Bereavement Committee organise an annual memorial service, now held in Dublin Castle, for all families who have lost children in the hospital in the preceding year. In respect of the burial of organs, the hospital follow guidelines developed in the HSE for any such enquiries.

10 Are there still ninety-eight sets of organs in the hospital as reported?

Once the hospital became aware of publicity surrounding organ retention in Bristol in 1999, a decision was made that no organs retained in the hospital would be disposed of without specific instructions from the family. This decision was subsequently endorsed by the National Committee for Organ Retention in the UK and the Madden Report recommendations and remains the position of the hospital. However, it is anticipated that the publication of the forthcoming national HSE audit on post mortem practice will allow hospitals who hold organs from post mortems where the families have not contacted the hospital, despite the extensive publicity on this issue, to finally dispose of them in a dignified manner. It is hoped that this mechanism would also allow the retrieval of the organs should a family ever return to the hospital in the future.

Our Lady's very much follow the guidelines of the HSE, which made it a little difficult to get direct answers from them. The guidelines to which Our Lady's refer to can be found on the HSE website (www.hse.ie).

Holles Street

Peter Boylan, former Master of Holles Street with thirty years' experience, answered my questions:

1 *Now in Holles Street things are incredibly detailed with parents involved at all levels. For example, now we even give parents tissue document lists if tissues are retained.*

2 *We now explain exactly what the post mortem process is to parents so they have full consent of it. This is usually done by a consultant pathologist.*

3 *We have bereavement personnel now on the staff.*

4   *Informed consent also means that a consent form is used for permission to conduct an autopsy and is now signed by the parent(s).*

5   *The biggest difference since the scandal without doubt is the attitude on the part of staff and parents. There is far more transparency now and patients know they can come to us at any time to ask a question.*

The Coombe

Chris Fitzpatrick, Master of Ireland's busiest maternity hospital (delivering over 8,500 babies annually) took time out from his hectic schedule, just before going into theatre, to have a chat and answer a few of my questions. The Coombe's website is well worth a view; it is listed at the back of the book.

1   How is the news broken to someone who rings and asks if their baby's organs are there?

   There is a very co-ordinated response. They will be put straight through to our Patient Service Unit and from here they will be put through to me.

2   What is the biggest lesson the hospital has learned from the scandal?

   To put the patient/parent at the centre of care; that is pivotal. The HSE is making positive strides to put the patient at the centre of the treatment.

3 Is there more informed consent and communication with patients now?

Absolutely. There is a significant improvement in terms of consent. The expectation on behalf of parents and relatives is discussed with empathy and accuracy. We try to be as gentle as we can be when giving distressing news.

When it comes to post mortems we don't have to achieve consent first time around. We now give them the consent forms and then give them the time to digest what they have been told and to read over the forms. This can take between twenty-four and forty-eight hours.

We all learn from experience. Whether at consultant or specialist level or as an intern just graduating, we all need to be aware of the need for compassion and empathy.

4 What do you think caused the scandal?

I don't really think it was any one thing, nor do I believe it was done with any ill-intent on the parts of those directly involved. I think it was done for the right reasons in the wrong way and in so doing caused a lot of pain to parents. Truth is a very important part of medical care. As a medical society we didn't deal with the scandal very well and I admit that we didn't impart information properly. These days we are far better equipped to deal with explaining surgery to patients. We have worked very hard to rebuild trust but I think we have succeeded. Trust was compromised and we can't expect for it to return overnight. We worked hard and our hard work paid off. We have all been patients or relatives of patients so we do have an insight from "the other side" so to speak.

5   What is the biggest change the scandal has prompted?

Prior to this there was an increasing formalisation of the post mortem process. We have continued to evaluate this and more importantly we look carefully at how we care for our patients in the post bereavement process. We never discharge a woman who has lost a baby. Even after the final bereavement meeting they know that if they have a question in three weeks, three months, three years or thirty years, they can contact us and we will answer it for them.

6   Do you think there should be more accountability regarding the scandal?

I think that accountability should be shared across the profession. If no harm was intended then the medical profession should say sorry to those affected.

CHAPTER 11

Clement's Story:
Our Little Ray of Sunshine

"If we don't stand up for children, then we don't stand for much."

MARIAN WRIGHT EDELMAN

Little Jessica Murphy was born on 13th June 1998 to Clement and Jacinta Murphy from Wexford. The couple were besotted with their daughter, who they said made their lives complete. She was everything they wished for and her father Clement said that a ray of light often surrounded her, which people commented on. He takes up the story.

Jessica was a very content baby. She was very placid and would look straight at you when you spoke to her, with a very intent expression on her face. It was most unusual for a child so young. Jessica had a hole in the heart, so hospital visits quickly became part of our routine. On 9th

203

September we brought her to Holles Street for a routine visit. They said she was putting on weight and appeared to be thriving. However, when we brought her to Our Lady's Hospital in Crumlin, Dublin, less than a week later, the doctor there said she was very sick. They let us bring her home for a while, but we were told that she needed surgery and we would have to return.

When we returned to the hospital it was decided that Jessica needed to undergo two operations, such was the size of the hole in her heart. The first operation was the artery banding (a temporary measure to fix the defect). The second would be to repair the hole. The whole thing was so unreal and like all parents who are told their baby is sick, we were extremely worried.

However, after only two days she developed pneumonia, which meant they couldn't do the operation. She was in the intensive care unit for ages and as she kept getting infections she had to be quarantined, which meant the operation was constantly being postponed. Even through all of this Jessica continued smiling and soon became much loved by all the nurses, who would often bring her into the nurses' station. She was a real Daddy's girl, though, and I used to sing to her every night.

I was worried they were leaving it too late and we kept asking when she was going to have the surgery. She had already been there three months. I asked if she could have the surgery in the UK, and was very shocked when I was informed that Jessica had been removed from the list for this surgery in the UK because the hospital apparently didn't have enough experience.

I could not believe what I was being told. All this time Jacinta and I had assumed everything possible was being done for Jessica and by removing her name from the waiting list it seemed to us she had less chance of surgery. At this point Jessica was very ill and it was decided that the band operation had to be carried out if she was to survive. After the operation we were told that it didn't appear to be working very well and that they may have to reverse it. We thought they would do the major operation because Jessica was so ill and was deteriorating before our eyes. She had also developed eczema.

However, she never really woke up from the operation and was on a respirator. I was sitting with her one day; Jacinta had been there and I came in to give her a break. That was how we worked it. Anyway, I was fairly familiar with reading the machines. I watched the machine intently for a while and when I saw nothing was changing I decided to join Jacinta for a cup of tea in the canteen.

I had just sat down when a nurse called us and told us that they were trying to revive Jessica. What? I had only just left her bedside and she was fine. There must be some mistake, I thought to myself, as we rushed through the hospital to Jessica. We were too late. They hadn't been able to revive her. It was with sheer disbelief that we stood there, too shocked to say very much at first. We were so devastated; it just didn't seem right. We spent some time on our own with Jessica. Then we were brought to a room and given tea and biscuits.

We still hadn't come to terms with what had happened when we were asked if they could perform an autopsy.

We said "yes" in the hope that something would be found that might help other parents. Jessica's funeral was a tragic affair and life was never the same after she died. We didn't have any other children, so Jessica's death left such a huge void in our lives.

At this point, Jacinta takes up the story and explains how they were affected by the organ retention scandal.

I was listening to the radio and a woman called Margaret McKeever was on talking about the organ retention scandal. I jotted down the number she gave out and put it away. I mulled it over in my head for a few days and we talked about it. I remember saying to Clem that they couldn't have done that to Jessica.

It was a week later that I plucked up enough courage to ring Margaret, who was lovely and advised me to contact Crumlin directly. Neither of us really wanted to make this call, so we waited a few weeks. Eventually I contacted them and they told me that someone would be back in touch with me. We were asked if we would like to go into the hospital, or receive information by letter or by telephone. We opted for telephone. After about three weeks the doctor phoned us and went through it all with us. He explained that organs were usually incinerated, but we were "lucky" because they still had Jessica's organs in Crumlin. We then had to endure three long weeks of stress; of waiting every day to get the call that we could get her organs.

Jessica died on 17th December 1998, aged just six months. She had brought us so much joy in her short life and we wanted all of her back. It was April 1999 when eventually they asked if we wanted them to bury the organs, we said no. Clem went into the hospital to collect them and he brought them home. We have to believe what they told us is true, otherwise we would never really know if the heart and lungs we buried were Jessica's. It was so traumatic to have to bury Jessica for a second time; we knew it was something we could never do again.

In 2007 we again wrote to the hospital and were horrified to be told that they still had fifty-two slides and tissue samples belonging to Jessica. It was like history was repeating itself. We chose not to bury them; it was just far too traumatic. We asked if they could guarantee that there was no more of Jessica; we were told that the only guarantee they could give was that there was no more of Jessica at Crumlin.

We had to go looking for her heart and lungs and we couldn't understand why they didn't tell us at that point that there was more of Jessica still in the hospital. It would have saved us so much anguish.

I defy any person to tell me that what was done was done to "stop us suffering". By not giving us the answers, you are prolonging our agony. I have lost all faith in the system and believe the country is rotten to the core. Harsh words, perhaps, but it is how I feel. I am looking for answers; I am looking for the truth. Our Minister for Health doesn't appear to care very much about what happened. Anything else I have to say about her is not fit for print. In my opinion, the Government got together and decided to keep this scandal under wraps. *Give us the answers, we have waited long enough.*

CHAPTER 12

Politically Speaking

"On a personal level I would like to express my deepest sympathy for all those families, yours included, whose lives have been devastated by the retention of their children's organs without their consent. That their grief was compounded by a wall of silence from hospital authorities and a decade of seeking answers that are still denied is unpardonable."

EAMON GILMORE, TD, Leader of the Labour Party

Politicians are people too: grandparents, mothers, fathers, sisters, brothers, aunts, uncles, sons and daughters. Many of them have known the grief of burying loved ones. Their support for this publication has been staggering – with the exception of those at the epicentre: Ministers for Health Mary Harney and Brian Cowen, now Taoiseach. Surely, in a book such as this, which outlines a national scandal that has lasted a decade and cost millions of euro just to have boxes sit in a warehouse, is worthy of explanation and justification, not just to the parents and loved ones of the victims, but to their Dáil colleagues and the Irish public as well? After all, it is taxpayers' money and *somebody has to be held accountable* for establishing the first Inquiry in the history of the state that has not produced a publishable report.

These may be politicians, but I wondered what they were like as human beings. There is not one politician in Dáil Éireann today who can stand up and claim they do not know about the organ retention scandal, which has been debated for the past decade. I made sure of that by writing to them. What did they have to say about the scandal? Plenty.

Questions I asked:

1 *Like many others, I believe Government needs to introduce legislation governing human tissue to eliminate the possibility of something like this from ever happening again. What are your views?*

2 *Why, in your opinion, has the Dunne Inquiry never been made public? Will it be made public?*

3 *Why do you think the Madden Report omitted so much detail from the Dunne Inquiry?*

4 *What, in your opinion, is the reason for a public inquiry being refused?*

5 *How can the Government assure the public this will never happen again, when a decade later the Dunne Report is still sitting in a warehouse and we still have no answers?*

The replies varied, but there was the rarity of all-party agreement that answers are needed and legislation needs to be introduced without further delay. I have picked a sample of replies I received and I would like to take this opportunity to thank all those who responded; I was honestly overwhelmed at the huge number of replies I received and the encouragement I was given. I apologise if I have not had space to include your reply, but thank you for sending it and for your support. In time I will personally be in touch with each of you.

I have decided to leave out replies that used the specially prepared press release for me compiled by the Department of Health and Children, which you can read at the end of this chapter. I felt if they didn't have their own opinion on the scandal, then there was little point duplicating the same response again and again when it wasn't even their own.

I have, for the most part, left the replies essentially as received because I feel it brings a sense of reality and personality the reader will understand. They are not "standard" letters with stamped signatures, as so often received by people; these are replies from the heart, and not just the political heart. They are a combination of anger, frustration and, of course, sadness. Many of these politicians are themselves parents; and as such this particular scandal has touched a nerve that other scandals have not.

To me, this in itself is rather strange, when so many people sympathise, yet so very little is being done. I welcome the opportunity to meet with any politician at any time and tell them exactly what this scandal has done to me and my family and then tell them there are thousands and thousands more who have been similarly affected. I have requested a meeting with Ms Harney and Mr Cowen; I wonder if I will get one? By the time this book hits the shelves and I start doing interviews, I will be able to answer this question.

Why these people have essentially chosen to remain silent over such a national, expensive and widespread scandal when Irish people are demanding answers is anybody's guess. I gave each ample opportunity to comment; I even offered to extend the deadline because I felt it was very important that the Minister for Health, in particular, should have had some input into this book.

More importantly, she should have *wanted* to have had input and an opportunity to explain her actions and her reasons for closing down the Dunne Inquiry without enacting phase two of it; for not providing more information to parents; or for not giving far more serious thought to having a public inquiry when so many have demanded one.

Ireland is one of only two countries in the Western world with no human tissue act – the other is Malta. This is a fact backed up by the Department of Health, whom I questioned about it: "Ireland does not currently have a human tissue act. Work is currently underway at drafting the general scheme of a Human Tissue Bill, which will be submitted to Government when completed and, subject to their approval, will form the basis of a Human Tissue Bill." I believe the length of time this could take is anyone's guess.

Micheál Martin was Minister for Health and Children from 2000 to 2004, in the absolute epicentre of this scandal. He sent me a letter; his reply was a replication of the prepared press release that so many TDs chose to use.

I thought it was a particular shame because he could have contributed so very much given his position at the time, as could Mary Harney and Brian Cowen.

In June 2008, the *Sunday Independent* commented as follows:

> *In closing down the Dunne Inquiry, the Minister and her Department, including her Chief Medical Officer, closed down the chance of investigating – one way or the other – relationships between doctors and institutions with international companies as well as the sheer housekeeping duty of finding out what happened about organ retention in most hospitals, that is, the many more than the three surveyed by Dr Madden.*
>
> *In January 2008, Minister Harney ruled out giving families any compensation at all. Then she denied them the basic courtesy of seeing the Madden Report before every ordinary Joe out there. By refusing to publish the Dunne Report, she forced the families to pay to get such basic information. She and her officials didn't even give them the price of the stamp. Believe it or not, no one can say for sure who owns a dead Irish body or any part of it. Your body is not your own. And ten years after the scandal broke, the Government still hasn't regulated post-mortems on a statutory basis. The arrogance noticed by Dunne's report stretches way beyond hospital doors.*
>
> *(Reproduced with kind permission of the* Sunday Independent, *6th June 2007.)*

Eamon Gilmore, TD, Leader of the Labour Party, is very sympathetic to the cause and explained:

> In 2006, following the publication of the Madden Report Deputy Liz McManus questioned the then Taoiseach as to when the human tissues legislation would be introduced. The response, "The Bill is not listed on the legislative programme", must have been an affront to all those who had accepted the Government's promise to legislate. To this day the Government is not able to indicate when legislation will be published.

TD Billy Timmins expresses concern at the lack of legislation:

> I do believe that legislation is necessary to ensure there is not a reoccurrence of the issues you outlined. I am aware that the practices involved have caused great distress to many and I deeply regret what took place. Unfortunately until such a time as legislation is put in place, one is always concerned that this could still be happening.

Tom Kitt, TD, had very strong views about the scandal, citing it as a *shameful act.*

> I believe that the organ retention scandal is one of the greatest scandals of our time and everything possible must be done to bring closure on the matter for the many families and next of kin affected by what happened at the time. I agree that the Government

needs to introduce legislation as promised governing human tissue to eliminate the possibility of something like this happening again . . .

Not knowing too much about the scandal, but wanting to seek the right information, Joe Behan, TD, wrote directly to the Minister for Health for assistance with the matter:

I note with interest and concern your comments regarding the organ retention scandal. I have written to the Minister for Health, Mary Harney, TD asking the questions you have asked me. I will revert to you when I receive her response. I attach a copy of my letter to her.

Minister for Health & Children
Department of Health & Children
Hawkins House
Hawkins Street
Dublin 2

Dear Mary

I have recently received correspondence from Ms Karina Colgan regarding her new book, which is soon to be published on the subject of organ retention. She asks questions to which she requires immediate answers. [The questions are at the start of this chapter.]

I would appreciate it if, having considered the questions raised by Ms Colgan, you could let me have your reply as soon as possible so that I can communicate this to Ms Colgan.

Yours sincerely,
Joe Behan TD

In response, Joe, like so many others, received a standard reply saying the matter was receiving attention.

Caoimhghín Ó Caoláin TD spoke on behalf of fellow Sinn Féin TDs Aengus Ó Snodaigh, Arthur Morgan and Martin Ferris and Senator Pearse Doherty, all of whom had very strong opinions on the scandal and were of the opinion that legislation is long overdue and the Dunne Report should have been published a long time ago.

I fully support the demand for legislation governing the use of human tissue and to ensure that the ordeal of so many families is never repeated. In October 2002 I tabled a Dáil motion on organ retention on behalf of the Technical Group (Sinn Féin, Green Party, Independents). The motion was debated for three and a half hours and called on the Government, among other demands, to publish a human tissue act, which would regulate by statute the practice of pathology within the State.

There is no valid excuse for the non-publication of the report of the Dunne Inquiry. I have called publicly for the Report to be released and this should be done. The release of the summary of the report to Parents for Justice under the Freedom of Information Act underlined the need to publish the Report in full. It must and will be made public, if sufficient pressure is exerted.

When I asked why they thought a public inquiry has been consistently refused, the Sinn Féin representatives were quick to reply:

The Government has offered no plausible reason for refusing a public inquiry. It has failed the bereaved parents in its whole approach to this issue. All of this could have been avoided had the Government accepted the October 2002 Dáil motion to which I have referred. That motion called for a public inquiry to be established and to complete its work 'in as comprehensive, economical and speedy a manner as possible'. The public inquiry could have been long completed at this stage.

When I questioned why the Madden Report omitted so much detail from the Dunne Inquiry they were scathing in their reply:

Again there is no valid excuse for concealment and I can only conclude that vested interests are being protected.

I asked them what they thought the solution was:

> *The best assurance is to put in place openness and accountability in the delivery of health services and a complete break with the legacy of the past where secrecy so often protected vested interests and patients' rights and those of bereaved relatives came second.*

Andrew Doyle, TD, himself a bereaved parent, had his own views:

> *I fully support the introduction of legislation, which would prevent organs being retained for any purpose without the full knowledge and consent of the parents, no matter what arguments are made otherwise.*
>
> *The Dunne Enquiry should be made public. I can't explain why the Madden report was so scant, except to surmise that it was in order to limit the "damage" to those responsible.*
>
> *Legislation will do a lot to prevent a reoccurrence of this type of episode and the medical profession's closing of ranks in this manner. Something else that should also be considered is a Patient Safety Charter, which might be overlooked by a body, which should include members of the medical and nursing professions, lay people and some public representatives.*
>
> *We were kicked off Health Boards and told it was to effect great efficiency and to do away with*

parochial politics – a fact I dispute strongly, as I feel we were the eyes and ears of the public and I cite the Blood Transfusion Board scandal, which had no political accountability, and we see the results.

Eamon Ryan, TD, was honest enough to say this issue was beyond his remit but promised to exert pressure on those who were in a position to do something:

I thank you for your email and commend you on your publications to date as well as on your forthcoming work.

While the tragic subject of your work goes beyond the remit of this office, I will endeavour to raise the issues you highlight with my colleagues in Government and particularly with the Minister for Health.

Tommy Broughan, TD, also promised to apply pressure in an effort to see that progress is made expeditiously.

Thank you very much for your email and briefing on the organ retention scandal and on your forthcoming book on the matter.

I agree completely with your comments that this was a barbaric and appalling scandal, and that parents were treated in a completely unacceptable and totally arrogant way.

I will again liaise with my colleagues in the Parliamentary Labour Party and Labour's Health

Spokesperson Deputy Jan O'Sullivan on this matter and bring all of the points that you noted in your email to her attention. You can be assured that the Labour Party will continue to pressure Minister Mary Harney until she finally addresses all of these important issues. Please keep in touch.

Minister Peter Power, not being totally sure of the facts, vowed to seek information: "I have asked Minister Mary Harney to prepare a briefing in relation to the important issues which you have raised in your email at which stage I will be in a better position to report back to you."

Leader of Fine Gael, Enda Kenny, TD, was less vocal. After initially telling me – in an email that was past deadline – that he had helped PFJ in the past and that all they wanted was truth, he ignored my questions despite the offer of an extended deadline. My final communication with him was as follows:

Dear Mr Kenny,

I am particularly surprised, as leader of the opposition, by your lack of response to my email of 29th August. The organ retention scandal is a matter of public concern and your lack of comment is surprising when so many other members of your party responded. It is regrettable there will be no comment from you.

Mise le meas,
Karina Colgan

I end with the response from Jan O'Sullivan, Labour Spokesperson on Health. It gives one reason to pause for thought.

Dear Karina,

Thank you very much for your email in relation to the book you are writing on the organ retention scandal. It has also been forwarded to me from my colleagues for reply on behalf of the party. The enclosed reply is on behalf of the Labour Party and from myself as spokesperson on Health. Congratulations on writing about this very important issue and I hope the book will be read by a large number of people.

I will, as spokesperson, continue to work with Parents for Justice, to ensure that the truth is published and that such a scandal can never happen again.

Response to Questions:

1 *I believe the Government needs to introduce legislation governing human tissue to ensure that what occurred in the past never happens again. I will continue to press for this legislation in the Dáil.*

2 *The explanations given as to why the Dunne Inquiry was not made public are not acceptable. The information that has subsequently been acquired by Parents for Justice, through the*

Freedom of Information Act, indicates that there is a great deal of material that could and should be published in the public interest.

3 *I am not directly aware of why the Madden Report omitted so much of the detail from the Dunne Inquiry. We need to have a comprehensive examination of the entire material in order to throw some light on what is a very confusing and very expensive and unsatisfactory process so far.*

4 *There has been no satisfactory explanation as to why a public inquiry was refused.*

5 *The best way of ensuring that this will never happen again is to throw light on what happened in the past and to ensure that appropriate legislation is enacted for the future.*

Despite all the time and money spent over the past decade there has been neither clarification nor closure for families in relation to the organ retention scandal. The issue just cannot be left with so many outstanding questions.

Spin Doctoring

A press release was written by the Department of Health and Children for TDs to use to answer my questions, which is reproduced below verbatim. I haven't reproduced the response of any TDs who chose to use this as their reply, who included previous Minister for Health at the time of the scandal, Micheál Martin, who promised so much and ultimately did so little.

Title: Response to queries raised by Ms Karina Colgan, September, 2008

Questions

1 *Like many others, I believe Government needs to introduce legislation governing human tissue to eliminate the possibility of something like this from ever happening again. What are your views?*

- Legislative proposals are being developed to meet the key recommendation of the Madden Report that no post mortem examination should be carried out and no tissue retained for any purpose whatsoever without authorisation. The scope of the proposed legislation will cover the removal, retention, storage, use and disposal of human tissue from deceased persons, and related matters. Proposals on the scope of the legislation have been approved by the Minister and a Memorandum will be submitted to Government shortly seeking approval to draft the general scheme and heads of the Bill.

- A public consultation process has been initiated and discussions have been held with the key stakeholders. A Consultative Forum on the development of the legislative proposals was held in June 2007 followed by a public invitation for written submissions. The analysis of submissions received in response to the consultation process has been completed and discussions are ongoing with the major stakeholders on issues identified from the submissions. The consultation process will continue while the general scheme is being drafted (subject to Government approval), and further public consultation will be held on the draft Scheme and Heads of Bill.

2 *Why has the Dunne Inquiry never been made public? Will it be made public?*

- The report of the Inquiry into post mortem practice and organ retention chaired by Anne Dunne was presented to the Minister in March 2005. The advice of the Attorney General, however, was that it could not be published for legal reasons.

- Some sections of Dunne Report Executive Summary, containing recommendations and principal findings, were released in 2006 under FOI Acts. Following internal review, redacted version of Executive Summary was released on 14/02/2008, containing more specific points of detail.

- In the light of the legal advice given by the Attorney General there are no plans to publish the full report produced by Ms Anne Dunne SC.

3 *Why did the Madden Report omit so much detail from the Dunne Inquiry?*

- Dr Deirdre Madden, a distinguished expert on medical law, was appointed by Government in May 2005 to provide a report on key issues in paediatric post mortem practice and procedures. Her terms of reference were:

  1 To inquire into policies and practices relating to the removal, retention and disposal of organs from children who have undergone post mortem examination in the State since 1970;

  2 To inquire into allegations that pituitary glands were removed from children undergoing post mortem examination for sale to pharmaceutical companies within and outside the State;

  3 To examine professional practice in relation to the information given to children's parents in respect of the removal, retention and disposal of tissue and organs and the appropriateness of practices of obtaining consent;

  4 To review the manner in which hospitals responded to concerns raised by bereaved families relating to post mortem practices carried out on children;

  5 To make recommendations for any legislative and/or policy change as deemed appropriate.

- Dr Madden had access to all of the documentation assembled by the Dunne Inquiry. Her report, containing fifty recommendations and a number of findings, was published on 18th January 2006. The Minister is satisfied that Dr Madden took all relevant matters into consideration in drafting her report and that she has produced a robust and thorough evaluation of the papers she examined.

- The key findings in the Madden Report were as follows:

  o Post mortem examinations were carried out according to best professional and international standards and no intentional disrespect was shown to deceased children or their families.

  o Communication between hospital staff and parents and next of kin was poor, with people not being told that organs might be retained at a post mortem. This was often done for paternalistic reasons, where doctors did not wish to upset next of kin when they were already distressed and vulnerable.

  o There was no legislative framework in place and no consistent national policy relating to these practices. However, the lack of a national policy on post mortem practice until 2002 is not unique to Ireland, nor was it the usual practice in other countries to provide information about organ retention to relatives of a deceased person.

o In some cases it may have been necessary to send samples of organs or tissues to hospitals in other countries for specialist examination.

o The system of disposal of organs and tissues by hospitals was not intentionally disrespectful to children or their families. Hospitals were constrained by health and safety regulations and were obliged to consider organs and tissues as clinical waste. In this context, because there were no appropriate facilities in Ireland this material had to be sent to other countries for appropriate disposal in accordance with health and safety legislation.

The Madden Report was followed by a working group, chaired by Dr Madden, which addressed issues relating to post mortems on babies who died before or during birth, minors over the age of twelve and adults.

• One of the key recommendations of the report was that a working group be established to examine issues not included in the original terms of reference, i.e. post mortem issues relating to babies who died before or during birth, minors and adults. This group, chaired by Dr Madden, was set up in March 2006 and its membership included representatives of Parents for Justice and the Irish Stillbirth and Neonatal Death Society, together with healthcare professionals from a range of disciplines. The report from the working group was published on 7th November 2006. The working group report endorsed the recommendations made in the Madden Report, in particular the need for legislation.

4 *What is the reason for a public inquiry being refused?*

- The Minister has indicated to the Dáil that there is nothing to be gained from a further statutory inquiry. Dr Madden's report concluded that *"the best resolution of this issue for bereaved parents is to enact clear and unambiguous legislation to ensure that such practices cannot happen again in the future without their knowledge and authorisation."* The Minister's position is that she has accepted Dr Madden's Report, and the focus of the Department must now be to support the work of the Health Service Executive in implementing the recommendations, and to make progress on proposals for human tissue legislation.

- Parents for Justice have referred in previous correspondence to a letter which they received from DoHC on 27th September 2000 which stated, among other things, that *"the Minister has confirmed that in the most unlikely event of the Inquiry not meeting its objectives in this regard, he will pursue the establishment of alternative forms of inquiry, including the establishment of a statutory inquiry under the Tribunal Acts, if necessary."* However, the establishment of a statutory inquiry was only one option cited as an *"alternative form of inquiry"*.

- In effect, the report by Dr Madden, who had access to all of the documentation assembled by the Dunne Inquiry, met the objectives agreed by the Government for the completion of the inquiry process.

5 *How can you assure the public this will never happen again?*

- Public concern in relation to the unauthorised removal and retention of the organs of deceased patients is acknowledged and the grief and suffering to families is deeply regretted.

- The aim is now to ensure that the health service response at the time of loss is one of best practice, which treats the deceased and their loved ones with dignity and respect.

- As outlined above, legislative proposals are being developed to meet the key recommendation of the Madden Report and Working Group Report that no post mortem examination should be carried out and no tissue retained for any purpose whatsoever without authorisation.

- Considerable progress has been made by the Health Service Executive in implementing the other recommendations of the Madden Report and the Department will continue to liaise with the HSE in this regard.

CHAPTER 13

A Papal Perspective

"This law has as its first and general principle, 'to do good and to avoid evil'."

HIS HOLINESS, POPE BENEDICT XVI

I thought this was a particularly apt comment to begin with from His Holiness, because I talk about evil in my own introduction. I felt it would be interesting to see if I could get a response or comment from the Pope, primarily because on these kinds of issues the Vatican generally tends to remain silent. However, it would appear that it is starting to address some of the issues of the twenty-first century, which can't be a bad thing.

Unfortunately I was unable to get a comment from Archbishop Diarmuid Martin, but I feel that this adequately compensates. Like most people, the Pope condemns unauthorised organ retention and rightly so. However, he is in favour of authorised tissue and organ transplants in order to give life to another. He slates organ abuse and trafficking and urges people to reject such unacceptable practices.

What he had to say was both interesting and informative and I feel that the Church has come a long way and is making a concerted effort to embrace and address the issues of the twenty-first century. His reply was not at all what I was expecting; it was very informative and, dare I say, very "with it".

"Organ donation is a peculiar form of witness to charity. In a period like ours, often marked by various forms of selfishness, it is ever more urgent to understand how the logic of free giving is vital to a correct conception of life. Indeed, a responsibility of love and charity exist that commits one to make of their own life a gift to others, if one truly wishes to fulfil oneself. As the Lord Jesus taught us, only whoever gives his own life, can save it (cf. Luke 9:24).

"Medical history clearly shows the great progress that it has been possible to accomplish to ensure to each person who suffers an evermore worthy life.

"Tissue and organ transplants represent a great victory for medical science and are certainly a sign of hope for many patients who are experiencing grave and sometimes extreme clinical situations.

"If we broaden our gaze to the entire world it is easy to identify the many and complex cases in which, thanks to the technique of the transplantation of organs, many people have survived very critical phases and have been restored to the joy of life.

"This could never have happened if the committed doctors and qualified researchers had not been able to count on the generosity and altruism of those who have donated their organs. The problem of the availability of vital organs to transplant, unfortunately, is not theoretic, but dramatically practical; it is shown by the long waiting lists of many sick people whose sole possibility for survival is linked to the meagre offers that do not correspond to the objective need.

"It is helpful, above all in today's context, to return to reflect on this scientific breakthrough, to prevent the multiple requests for transplants from subverting the ethical principles that are at its base. As I said in my first encyclical, the body can never be considered a mere object (cf. *Deus Caritas Est*, n. 5); otherwise the logic of the market would gain the upper hand.

"The body of each person, together with the spirit that has been given to each one singly constitutes an inseparable unity in which the image of God himself is imprinted. Presiding from this dimension leads to a perspective incapable of grasping the totality of the mystery present in each one.

"Therefore, it is necessary to put respect for the dignity of the person and the protection of his/her personal identity in the first place.

"As regards the practice of organ transplants, it means that someone can give only if he/she is not placing his/her own health and identity in serious danger, and only for a morally valid and proportional reason.

"The possibility of organ sales, as well as the adoption of discriminatory and utilitarian criteria, would greatly clash with the underlying meaning of the gift that would place it out of consideration, qualifying it as a morally illicit act.

"Transplant abuses and their trafficking, which often involve innocent people like babies, must find the scientific and medical community ready to unite in rejecting such unacceptable practices.

"Therefore they are to be decisively condemned as abominable. The same ethical principle is to be repeated when one wishes to touch upon creation and destroy the human embryo destined for a therapeutic purpose. The simple idea of considering the embryo as "therapeutic material" contradicts the cultural, civil and ethical foundations upon which the dignity of the person rests.

"It often happens that organ transplantation techniques take place with a totally free act on the part of the parents of the patients in which death has been certified. In these cases, informed consent is the condition subject to freedom, for the transplant to have the characteristic of a gift and *is not* to be interpreted as an act of coercion or exploitation.

"It is helpful to remember, however, that the individual vital organs cannot be extracted except *ex cadaver*, which, moreover, possesses its own dignity that must be respected.

"In these years science has accomplished further progress in certifying the death of the patient. It is good, therefore, that the results attained receive the consent of the entire scientific community in order to further research for solutions that give certainty to all.

"In an area such as this, in fact, there cannot be the slightest suspicion of arbitration and where certainty has not been attained the principle of precaution must prevail. This is why it is useful to promote research and interdisciplinary reflection to place public opinion before the most transparent truth on the anthropological, social, ethical and juridical implications of the practice of transplantation.

"However, in these cases the principal criteria of respect for the life of the donator must always prevail so that the extraction of organs be performed only in the case of his/her true death (cf. *Compendium of the Catechism of the Catholic Church* n. 476).

"The act of love, which is expressed with the gift on one's vital organs remains a genuine testimony of charity that is able to look beyond death so that life always wins. The recipient of this gesture must be well aware of its value. He is the receiver of a gift that goes far beyond the therapeutic benefit.

"In fact, what he/she received, before being an organ, is a witness of love that must raise an equally generous response, so as to increase the culture of gift and gratuity.

"The right road to follow, until science is able to discover other new forms and more advanced therapies, must be the formation and the spreading of a culture of solidarity that is open to all and does not exclude anyone.

"A medical transplantation corresponds to an ethic of donation that demands on the part of all the commitment to invest every possible effort in formation and information, to make the conscience even more sensitive to an issue that directly touches the life of many people.

"Therefore it will be necessary to reject prejudices and misunderstandings, widespread indifference and fear to substitute them with certainty and guarantees in order to permit an even more heightened and diffuse awareness of the great gift of life in everyone.

"With these sentiments, while I wish each one to continue in his/her own commitment with the due competence and professionalism, I invoke the help of God on the Congress' works and I impart to all my warm blessing."

His Holiness, Benedict XVI

CHAPTER 14

Freda's Story:
Together Forever

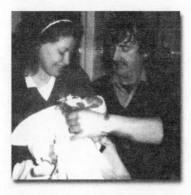

"Always leave room in your garden for the Angels to dance."

Unknown

(Author's note: *Sadly, we have no suitable photograph of Joanne's beautiful "big sister" Treasa Madeline, who was firstborn ten minutes earlier at 3.30 p.m. I feel it is more important that Treasa Madeline retains her dignity in death.*)

Like any new parents, Terry and Freda McGee couldn't wait for the arrival of their much-wanted and long-awaited child. Their son, who was ten, was equally excited to be getting a new brother or sister. Freda tells the story . . .

I was huge. I could barely walk and waddled around, but I loved the pregnancy nonetheless. One day I noticed I was losing water and a trace of blood. When I told them they admitted me and brought me for a scan. It quickly

237

became apparent that I was having twins. Oh, the excitement! Everyone was ecstatic because they were the only twins in the family. I was in hospital for a week before I finally went into labour.

I said I didn't want to give birth without my husband there, but there were so many people in the delivery suite, there simply wasn't room for him, so he waited outside. Treasa Madeline was born first at 3.30 p.m. on 13th December 1984 and was taken straight to ICU, without Terry catching as much as a glimpse of her. Joanne followed at 3.40 p.m. and the waters had to be broken for her birth. She was also rushed to ICU. I felt so sorry for Terry, who was outside waiting to see his babies, though he did manage to get a quick glimpse of Joanne.

We were in complete shock when a short time later we were told that Treasa Madeline had died. Mum and Terry were with me when we were told. Terry was allowed up to see her and hold her, but I wasn't; I was far too distraught and traumatised. All I kept thinking was that she was born on her birthday and she died on her birthday.

The next day I was brought up to see Joanne. Before going into the ICU, I was warned about all the tubes and machinery I would see and the noises I would hear. However, the only thing in the room I was aware of was my beautiful little baby girl Joanne lying in her incubator in front of me. I was allowed to touch her through the incubator and the staff were great.

Joanne was getting blood transfusions throughout and was fighting as hard as she could to survive. They allowed us to take her out of the incubator for the first time and, Lord, what a feeling. I will always cherish that memory and the photograph we had taken of the moment.

When they asked us if we wanted them to bury Treasa Madeline or if we wanted to have a private funeral, we opted for a private funeral; after all, this was a very private affair and we felt it should be for family and friends.

On the day I was going home, they brought me to see Treasa Madeline in the hospital church. She was in a little coffin and bound as far as her face. It was heartbreaking, but I was so very glad I had opted to do it. I went straight from the church to the undertakers, and then to my mother's to collect our son. It was only then we all broke down.

Joanne fought so hard and we spent so much time with her, just willing her on. We were in the hospital the day they decided to switch off the ventilator to give her the chance to breathe unassisted.

I didn't want to see this so I left the room and went to visit my mother. No sooner had I arrived at my mother's than the phone was ringing. It was bad news; Joanne had taken a turn for the worse and they asked me to return to the hospital.

I jumped on the train and I remember it being the longest journey of my life. Terry was there to meet me. When we got to the hospital, Terry gently told me that Joanne hadn't made it and had died. They put us into a private room and they brought her in to us. She was dressed in a white gown and had flowers in her hands. We were with her there for hours, looking at her as the tears ran down our faces. Our little fighter had given it her all, but in the end the odds were just too strong for her to overcome.

When we left, we went straight to the church and prayed. Then we went home. Everything became a blur and I lost track of what was going on around me. I pushed everyone and everything aside. One day Terry came to me and said, "I have lost two daughters and your son has lost his sisters." Somehow that was what it took for me to enter the real world again. It wasn't easy, but at least I was functioning again.

We buried them in the same grave so they would forever be together. We buried Treasa Madeline just before Christmas 1984 and Joanne on 5 January 1985. The funerals were a nightmare and I wouldn't wish them on anyone. Mother Nature doesn't intend for us to outlive our children and I had outlived two of mine. My son was very upset seeing us so upset.

In the weeks and months that followed, life went on, albeit differently. Then we became pregnant again and I was absolutely terrified. It was a normal pregnancy and birth and Siobhan was born on 11 November 1985. We went on to have another daughter, Áine, who was born in February 1987. Raising small children was hectic, but we enjoyed every moment of it and never complained after what we had been through.

In 2000, all hell broke loose when I saw something on the news about Alder Hey in the UK. I remember thinking to myself, "Those poor people." However, I pondered and pondered. I said to Terry that I had to find out, but I wasn't sure if it was something I wanted to know. In the end, we knew we had to know.

I rang the hospital helpline and spoke to a girl there. She said that if a post mortem had been carried out, *then it was more than likely that the girls' organs would be there.* She said she would check for me, and on 26th January 2001 we received a letter from the hospital "thanking" us for our enquiry regarding the possible retention of organ parts:

Having checked and rechecked your babies' files, in the case of your babies I can confirm organs were retained following their post mortems. I do appreciate how distressing this is for you and I am sorry if the factual nature of this letter adds further to your distress. However, I feel it is essential to be absolutely clear regarding your babies' circumstances. I would like to assure you that the hospital will retain your babies' organ parts until you have notified us of your wishes. A number of possible courses of action exist. Please find enclosed a form outlining a number of choices, which you may consider. Further details on which organs this hospital retained can be obtained by contacting the Hospital Co-ordinator.

I am sorry for the added distress this new information may cause you.

Yours sincerely,
Dr Declan Keane, Master

This was the letter we received in the post. I got the organs of both of my girls back and had them reburied with them. This was the first time I remember hearing that they had had a post mortem – I certainly don't remember being asked about one. That was another two burials and I was terrified I would see something when they opened the grave, but I didn't. At least now my girls were whole again. *Ten years on, I still don't have any answers. Why? What are they hiding?*

CHAPTER 15

How to Find Out if You are Affected

"Without struggle, there is no progress."
FREDERICK DOUGLASS

Organs/tissues are removed at a post mortem examination, which is normally carried out by a pathologist. There are two types of post mortem: a coroner's post mortem and a hospital post mortem. The vast majority of coroner's post mortems do not require permission from a relative. Hospital post mortems require permission from a relative and a consent form needs to be signed. However, up until relatively recently, it was quite common for permission to be given orally, with very little information being given to relatives about the procedure.

What makes the organ retention scandal different is that although many relatives gave permission for a post mortem to be performed on their loved one, they did not give permission for organs to be retained, lost, incinerated or left unused. Although many sought to ascertain if they were affected by the scandal when it first broke, others paid little attention, thinking it was confined to children or to Dublin and was essentially isolated to a few cases and happened years ago. However, as we now know, this is not the case. The practice was widespread, affected adults as well as children and continues to this day. At no point did the hospitals make contact with those affected; it was up to the victim's family to seek information, which wasn't always forthcoming.

I am a good example of how protracted and traumatic this process can be, but it was my choice to find out. I wanted to know what had happened to my son. I was not prepared for what I was told, nor for the duration of the process of burying him incomplete. While I wanted to know – or rather, needed to know – there are others who do not want to know and their wishes must be respected. However, there are also those who, after reading this book, may want to know, but don't know how to find out. This chapter will give you the information you need to find out whether or not a loved one of yours has been affected. It is not a complicated procedure, but you will need to have certain things before you begin. The decision on whether or not you want to find out is yours, but at least now you have the choice.

What You Will Need:

- The details of your child/relative's date of birth, date of death and full name and address at the time of death.

- A pen and notebook to record any conversations that you have. Always ask for the name of the person you speak to and also their position.

Record the date and time that you spoke to them and what was said. Also note if they say that they will call you back. Ask them *when* they expect to get back to you.

- You may be asked to send in your birth certificate. I was when I recently made enquiries about my father, who underwent a coroner's post mortem.

- Be persistent.

What to Ask

This is your opportunity to ask as many questions as you like. I would advise you to give the matter some thought rather than just instinctively picking up the telephone and being totally unprepared. There are some obvious questions you should ask and there are some less obvious. There may also be some personal questions that are not covered here. The most important thing to remember is, you have a right to have your questions answered and there is no limit imposed on the number of questions you ask or the number of times you ring for information.

Sometimes it helps to sit down in a quiet room with a pen and paper and write down every question you can think of and then, if applicable, ask your partner to do the same thing. You will be surprised at the different questions people have. After you have done this, put the notebook away and leave the matter aside for a few days. I know it will be hard, but looking at the notebook after a few days with a fresh pair of eyes often produces new questions.

Something else you should give some thought to is, if you have been affected, how do you want to be told? Some prefer by telephone; some prefer to go into the hospital; and others prefer by letter. I chose to go into the hospital the first time and by letter the second time, which was followed up by a meeting some time later. Always get the name of the person to whom you should speak and their telephone number/address should you have the need to ring back.

Possible Questions:

- Was it a hospital post mortem?

- Was it a coroner's post mortem?

- Why wasn't my informed consent sought?

- What organs/tissues were retained?

- Whose decision was it to retain organs/tissue?

- Why were they retained?

- Are they still kept at the hospital?

- Have they been transferred to another hospital?

- *Have* they been disposed of?

- How were they disposed of?

- *When* were they disposed of?

- *Where* are they now?

- Are they still being used at the hospital for anything?

- Is informed consent now sought?

- How many organs have they now got in the hospital?

- Have the next of kin been informed the organs are there?

- How is the issue of organ retention being dealt with now?

- How does the hospital/coroner (as appropriate) ensure that informed consent, based on real choice, is obtained before organs are retained?

- When did they introduce this new procedure?

- Do you have a designated bereavement counsellor on the staff?

Who to Ask

Ask to speak with the Chief Executive in the hospital where your child or relative died, or where the body had been taken. He or she is the person responsible for the running of the hospital. He or she may refer you to a helpline that they might have already set up to deal with enquiries. Don't be afraid to ask to speak with the Master either/as well. If the hospital has closed down, contact the Regional Health Authority for advice for which hospital to contact directly. If your child/relative had a coroner's post mortem, then contact the Coroner's Office directly. I went straight to the Master when I found out recently and the time prior to this went to the Head Social Worker. I know when I found out recently I opted to have the information given to me by letter. That way I could open it when I wanted to and not have to worry about anyone looking at my reaction to the content. However, I subsequently decided I also wanted to meet with them as I felt, and still feel, that my questions have not been properly addressed. I also have great difficulty in accepting that no records were kept.

Hard Choices

If you have been affected, there is no escaping the fact that you may have to make some difficult choices. I use the word "may" because in some cases parents still have no idea where their child's organs are; or in other cases the hospital took it upon themselves to incinerate the organs without contacting the parents.

If the organs are still in the hospital, then you have a number of options available to you:

- You can ask to have the organs physically returned to you, whereby you make your own arrangements for burial (any costs will be borne by the hospital).

- You can employ the services of an undertaker to carry out your wishes.

- You can ask to have the organs returned to you and arrange a burial (all expenses incurred will be borne by the hospital, who will also make all the arrangements and carry out your wishes if you so choose).

- You can ask the hospital to dispose of the organs in a dignified manner.

- You can ask the hospital to make the arrangements for the funeral on your behalf according to your wishes. Again all expenses will be met by the hospital.

Do not feel under pressure to make any immediate decisions if you don't feel up to it. It can take some time to absorb what is happening and more than likely you will be in shock, which will be compounded by grief. The hospital will retain the organs for as long as you want them to, even if it takes years.

Do not underestimate the shock of finding out that the child you thought you buried, was, in fact, only a shell. You have to be mentally prepared to hear some very unsavoury things. For example, your child's body may have been filled with sand to disguise the weight of the missing organs. Organs may be missing or have been incinerated unknown to you. The organ retention scandal is aptly named.

Burial

I buried my son with his grandparents because I didn't want him to be alone. We had to have the grave reopened to bury the casket containing the remains we recently received. In the case of all burial of organs, permission must be sought from and granted by the local council and church. Generally the person taking care of the funeral arrangements organises and obtains this. Paperwork from the hospital that verifies the organs belong to your loved one will also be required.

It is, however, worth noting that when a person has been cremated, organs cannot subsequently be buried. They may be cremated with the permission of the crematorium superintendent. As with a burial, paperwork from the hospital verifying that the organs belong to your loved one will also be required.

Of course, if it is the first death in the family and no organs have been retained you could consider purchasing a family plot.

Grieving

Grief works in strange ways and there is no right or wrong way to grieve. Allow yourself time to come to terms with what has happened and don't be surprised to find yourself bursting into tears at the unlikeliest of times. In time the raw pain will pass and you will never forget your precious loved one. Dwell not on the barbarity, but on their beauty.

For many bereavement counselling works well, which is why it was such a shock that the HSE elected to withdraw funding for this very necessary service last year. However, there are many ways counselling can be of benefit and I have listed a number of websites at the back of the book, all of which either provide counselling and answer questions online, or will direct you to where you can avail of it. For the most part they are free. The Samaritans are only a telephone call away if you think things are getting on top of you.

Don't expect to feel "back to normal" for quite a while; it takes time to heal. The intense pain vanishes, but don't be surprised to find yourself staring blankly at the television or forgetting what you have gone to the shops for. You will go through a range of emotions – all normal. Everything from anger and shock to heartbreak and desolation. There are physical ramifications to take into consideration as well, such as loss of sleep, loss of appetite, disinterest in anything and a general feeling of feeling unwell.

The Citizens Information Board has a leaflet that can be downloaded, which deals with information on matters following death.

Epilogue

It is only when you start researching the unauthorised organ retention scandal that you begin to realise the huge numbers of people involved and potentially involved. It is indeed of epidemic proportion and was endemic and unregulated for far too long, at far too great a cost in terms of human grief and suffering. This hasn't changed. The grief and suffering will go on until the answers that are so desperately needed to bring closure are given.

It is difficult to move forward when a system is moving backwards. However, that said, I am a firm believer in "people power" and I believe it is time to enforce what we, as a nation, are rightfully entitled to – accountability and truth. It is from the heart and on behalf of all those affected, and indeed those who may potentially be affected, that I ask you to help us get the answers we have been pleading for, for ten long years. Help us make our voices heard and join with us in our quest for truth and answers.

Politicians have strongly voiced their opinions in this book, yet they have been unable to enact change or have the Dunne Inquiry made public. Perhaps now they will exert a little more pressure knowing they are being held accountable, particularly when election time comes around. *Petition your local TD; write to the Minister for Health and Children, Mary Harney; or to the Taoiseach, Brian Cowen.*

If you would like to contact your TD, the email addresses of every sitting TD are available on the following website, which should make it a little easier for you:

http://oireachtas.ie/documents/members_emails/30_Dail.doc

There are plenty of websites which will give you template letters – just type "how to write to a politician" into Google and away you go! If you prefer putting pen to paper these are the key people to whom you should address your letter:

Mary Harney, TD
Minister for Health and Children
Hawkins House
Dublin 2.

Mr Brian Cowen, TD
Taoiseach
Dept of the Taoiseach
Government Buildings
Upper Merrion Street
Dublin 2.

You may not think it, but *you really can make a difference.* We have waited long enough for answers and truth – it is time for them to come out, for human tissue legislation to be enacted and for the Dunne Inquiry to be made public and that's just for starters. We also demand accountability for the money that changed hands. It's time for action, Mr Cowen and Ms Harney; we won't be going away until we get what we have been fighting a decade for. That's a promise.

Useful Websites

For this book I mainly used the Internet for research. The primary reason for this was because there is virtually nothing printed on the matter of unauthorised organ retention in Ireland, with the exception of the Madden Report, a few censored pages of the Dunne Inquiry and a number of rather aged Dáil debates and newspaper articles. There was by no means enough information upon which to base a book of this nature. Some of the sites I came across were invaluable, both as a mother and as a journalist. Some sites are easier to understand than others, so I chose to stick to the user-friendly sites for this section of the book.

www.amnch.ie *(National Children's Hospital, Tallaght)*

www.bioethics.ie *(Organs for Sale?)*

www.bmj.com *(British Medical Journal)*

www.caringinfo.org *(coping with grief)*

www.citizensinformation.ie/categories/death *(bereavement counselling & support)* www.cpsqa.ie *(Commission on Patient Safety and Quality Assurance)*

www.coombe.ie *(Coombe Women's and Infants University Hospital)*

www.coronerdublincity.ie *(Dublin City Coroner's Court)*

www.cso.ie *(Central Statistics Office, Ireland)*

www.discoveriesinmedicine.com

www.dohc.ie *(Department of Health and Children)*

www.dohc.ie/publications/madden.html *(downloadable Madden Report)*

foi@taoiseach.gov.ie *(Freedom of Information email)*

www.fsa.ie/parentingpositively/Death%20adults.pdf

www.helpguide.org/mental/grief_loss.htm

www.hse.ie *(Health Service Executive)*

www.ika.ie *(Irish Kidney Association)*

www.imba.ie/imba_article *(loss of child)*

www.imj.ie *(Irish Medical Journal)*

www.imo.ie *(Irish Medical Organisation)*

www.ino.ie *(Irish Nurses Organisation)*

www.irishhealth.ie *(patient support groups)*

www.irishhealth.com/article.html?id=10006 *(Irish doctors were arrogant)*

www.irishtimes.com/newspaper/breaking/2008/0714/breaking60.htm

www.justice.ie *(Department of Justice, Equality and Law Reform)*

www.lawcare.ie/griefandbereavement.doc

www.lawsociety.ie *(Law Society of Ireland)*

www.mlaw.ie/Organ-Retention

http://www.netautopsy.org/

www.ni4kids.com/features/ *(type "death of a child" into search facility)*

www.nmh.ie *(National Maternity Hospital, Holles Street)*

www.oireachtas.ie *(Human Body Organs and Tissues Bill 2008)*

www.olhsc.ie *(Our Lady's Children'sHospital, Crumlin)*

www.parentsforjustic.com *(Parents for Justice)*

press.office@taoiseach.gov.ie

www.rcsi.ie *(Royal College of Surgeons in Ireland)*

www.rip.ie *(advice and help)*

www.rotunda.ie *(Rotunda Hospital, Dublin)*

www.samaritans.ie *(for confidential and emotional support, available 24 hours a day.)*

www.sandsni.org/advice/whenYourBabyDies.html

www.tbiguide.com/dealingwithdoctors.html

www.vatican.com *(Vatican City website)*

www.veritas.ie *(counselling/bereavement)*

www.vhi.ie *(grief/bereavement)*

www.who.com *(World Health Organization)*

www.who.int/mediacentre/factsheets/fs180/en/(CJD)

http://en.wikipedia.org/wiki/Pituitary_gland

Bibliography

"Assisted reproduction in the Republic of Ireland – a legal quagmire", *Ethics, Law and Society: Volume 2*, Ashgate publishers (2006).

British Medical Journal, Archive of Disease in Childhood; 84:455–456 (June 2001).

British Medical Journal, "Alder Hey report condemns doctors, management, and coroner"; 322:255 (2001).

Cheney A, *Body Brokers: Inside America's Human Remains*, Broadway Books (2006).

Colgan, K, *If it Happens to You: Miscarriage & Stillbirth: A Human Insight*, A & A Farmar (2004).

Colgan, K, *Hear my Silence: Overcoming Depression*, Poolbeg Press (2008).

Combes, A, Mokhtari, M, Couvelard, A, *et al.,* "Clinical and autopsy diagnoses in the intensive care unit: a prospective study", *Archive of Internal Medicine,* 164 (4): 389–92 (2004).

"Consent needed for organ retention", *British Medical Journal*, 321:1098, 4 November 2000.

Croes, EA, Roks, G, Jansen, GH, Nijssen, PCG and van Duijn, CM, "Creutzfeldt-Jakob disease 38 years after diagnostic use of human growth hormone", *J. Neurol. Neurosurgery Psychiatry*, June 1; 72(6): 792–793 (2002).

Dept. of Health and Children, "Body and organ donation in Ireland – Post-mortems and organ retention" (1995).

Dooley, D, Dalla-Vorgia, P, *The Ethics of New Reproductive Technologies: Cases and Questions*, Berghahn Books (2003).

"Empowering Health Information: Medico-Legal Issues", *Medico-Legal Journal of Ireland*, Vol. 8 (1) 7–13 (2002).

European Tissue and Cells Directive (2004).

"Forensic pathology services quality must be guaranteed", *British Medical Journal*, June 15, 2002.

Hughes, NS, *The global traffic in human organs: A report presented to the House Sub Committee on International and Human Rights* (US Stats Council), 26 June 2001.

"Irish media revelations prompt revised post mortem guidelines", *The Lancet*, Vol. 355, Issue 9204, 19 February 2002.

"Legal status of archived human tissue", *Medico-Legal Journal of Ireland*, Vol. 10 (2) 76–83 (2004).

Madden, D, *Medicine, Ethics and the Law*, Butterworth 2002.

Madden, D, *Report on Post Mortem Practice and Procedure*, Government Publications Office (2006).

New York Times, 21 March 1994.

Nuremberg Trials Project, Harvard Law School Library (2003).

Page, Jeremy, Sam Lister and Anthony Browne (2005), "The research institute that advertises fetus body parts on internet", *The Times* (On-line), URL: http://www.timesonline.co.uk/article/0,,13509-1773726,00.html.

Roach, Mary, *Stiff: The Curious Lives of Human Cadavers*, WW Norton & Company (2003).

Swerdlow, AJ, Higgins, C.D, Adlard, P, Jones, ME, and Preece, MA, "Creutzfeldt-Jakob disease in United Kingdom patients treated with human pituitary growth hormone", *Neurology*, 23 September 2003.

World Health Organisation, *Digest of Health Legislation, Bibliography of Transport and Ethics*, Version 2.0, Geneva, Switzerland, 27 August 2004.